2

117

THE DRUG DILEMMA

McGRAW-HILL SERIES
IN HEALTH EDUCATION

DEOBOLD B. VAN DALEN, *Consulting Editor*

THE DRUG DILEMMA

SIDNEY COHEN, M.D.

Chief, Psychosomatic Medicine
Wadsworth Hospital
Veterans Administration Center
Los Angeles, California

McGRAW-HILL BOOK COMPANY

New York   St. Louis   San Francisco   Toronto   London   Sydney

HV
5801
.C57

THE DRUG DILEMMA

Copyright © 1969 by McGraw-Hill, Inc. All Rights Reserved.
Printed in the United States of America. No part of this
publication may be reproduced, stored in a retrieval system,
or transmitted, in any form or by any means, electronic,
mechanical, photocopying, recording, or otherwise, without
the prior written permission of the publisher.

Library of Congress Catalog Card Number 68-25649

234567890 VBVB 754321069

To **ILSE, DOROTHY,** *and* **RICHARD**

ALMA COLLEGE
MONTEITH LIBRARY
ALMA, MICHIGAN

PREFACE

The Drug Dilemma was designed for those who teach and counsel students. Since parents are intimately involved in their children's learning in important life situations and over prolonged periods, they may find relevant information about drug misuse here. But the book was not designed to exclude the student himself. Indeed, he is the ultimate consumer, whether it be directly by reading or indirectly by class or group discussion.

Obviously, young men and women have widely varying amounts of information about the mind-altering drugs. For that reason many levels of discussion are included, from the historical and physiological to the psychological and philosophic. It is hoped that most of the questions that arise have been answered, even when that answer can only be, "We don't know today." In fact, much of the material has been developed from questions asked by high school, college, and graduate students, by student health service personnel, and by deans of students.

Mind-altering drugs occupy a prominent place in the interests of students today. From the number of letters I receive requesting information, they must be first in popularity as a subject for English themes, science reports, and term papers. This curiosity is healthy, and we can only hope that factual material is available for students' consideration. It is not easy for the mass news media to be accurate without overemphasizing the novel and the sensational. Neither can we expect that those whose positions have polarized at one extreme or another will be reliably factual. No one is without some bias; I hope that mine has not distorted the information offered here.

SIDNEY COHEN

CONTENTS

INTRODUCTION

In a world undergoing enormous transitions, where familial and social supports are eroding and established beliefs are gradually being demolished, it is natural that many will try to modify their awareness—to ease the uncertainties of the day, to avoid psychic pain, to achieve pleasure, to find faith. The old gods falter; the old goals seem pointless. What is left but to chemically dull the senses or, alternatively, create new illusions, new utopian worlds? So it has been in every period of stress; so it is today.

Man changes his world enormously but himself minimally. He has created instant news, transportation that arrives before it has departed, and vast power from imploded atoms; but he remains the superb technological master concealing the impulsive, frightened child within. The training of his intellect has far exceeded the training of his emotions. His rational cerebral cortex outstrips his emotional midbrain.

This disparity between our emotional immaturity and the uncertainties of burgeoning power makes for a threatening and precarious existence. Some of us try to do something about the current predicament: We try to train ourselves and our children in emotional growth and discipline, and we attempt to reduce cruelty, correct injustice, counteract intolerance, prevent dehumanization, and protest against the mindless exploitation of nature. Others take another route: Their nerve fails, hopelessness prevails, and they proceed to withdraw from grinding frustrations. They egotistically seek the pleasures and demand the freedoms of the human encounter but refuse its responsibilities. This all can be done without drugs; with drugs it is so much easier.

These are only some of the reasons for the current upsurge of drug-taking behavior among the young in mind. The avoidance of life stress, the retreat from problem solving, the refusal to cope with adversity, the surrender to defeat, the quest for relevance, and "the death of God"—these and other perplexing situations call forth a search for pharmacological release.

Many of us suffer from a serious disease of affluence: directionlessness. No longer need large segments of this society focus on the struggle to avoid hunger, thirst, and the extremes of temperature which preoccupied their fathers. Unfortunately, new directions and new goals have not yet been acquired. Meanwhile, for others the crushing diseases of poverty remain, and these enhance escape in the form of a bedrugged existence. Although we cannot agree with the means, we can try to understand the attractiveness of oblivion, the distancing from hurt, or the fabulous fantasies that drugs can bring.

It is my belief that when a person becomes a "head,"—be it "pothead," "hophead," "acidhead," "pillhead," or "rumhead"—he has relinquished a core aspect of his existence. He has surrendered his human freedom, his individuation—the potion has become the master. Tillich would have said that his personal "centeredness" has been lost. To paraphrase the statement made about the person vulnerable to alcohol: First the person takes the drug, then the drug takes the person.

Naturally, as with drink, many kinds of drug users exist. But the illegality and the culture-alien aspects of drug usage make it more socially hazardous than the misuse of alcohol. Particularly, the biologically or psychologically unstable and the defeated will become overly involved in excessive taking of mind-altering substances. One is reminded of the fragment from Edgar Lee Masters's *Spoon River Anthology*:

> What is this I hear of sorrow and weariness
> Anger, discontent and drooping hopes?
> Degenerate sons and daughters
> Life is too strong for you
> It takes life to love Life.

THE DRUG DILEMMA

"THOSE WHO WILL NOT LEARN FROM HISTORY. . ."

CHAPTER ONE

Contrary to careless statements often heard, man is not the only creature that can become dependent upon drugs. Under artificial conditions almost any animal can become addicted, including mice, monkeys, and dogs. Under natural conditions animals tend to avoid intoxicating plants, but horses, cows, and sheep that have grazed on the locoweeds (*Astragalus mollisimus, Oxytropis spendens*, etc.) on the range develop a craving for these weeds. According to Lewin they become an "incurable slave of the passion." One such animal may "turn on" a whole flock by leading them to the locoweed and eating it in their presence. Interestingly, it is the young animal that is especially susceptible to both the intoxicating and debilitating effects of locoweeds.

Man has made strenuous efforts to find mind-altering substances and techniques. The ancient story of fermented honey, grains, and fruits needs no retelling here. Indian hemp and opium have been used for millennia. At times the discovered psychochemical appears to fit many of the needs of the culture. The coca leaf permitted the Andean Indian to work beyond his endurance in the low-oxygen atmosphere 2 miles high. The antifatigue, refreshing effects of the cocaine, extracted by chewing a cud of leaves mixed with ashes, sustained them in their bleak struggle for survival. The same alkaloid brought to Western Europe in the nineteenth century was a disaster to its middle-class users.

Availability is a prime consideration. Caapi was found by the Amazonian Indians. The iboga bean is gathered for the seething rituals of the Iboga and Oubanghi tribes of what was the French Congo. The Australian aborigine has the leaves of the energizing pituri plant at hand. These he mixes with ash and chews whenever he feels let down.

However, easy accessibility to a drug is not always a requirement for its entry into a culture. Pituri trails still can be seen in central Australia over which the aborigines transported the stimulating leaves for hundreds of miles to trade with other tribes. Khat (*Catha edulis*) is a mildly euphoriant plant. It grows in Ethiopia, and yet it is fairly universally chewed on the Arabian peninsula. Its transportation from Africa to Asia is a substantial factor in the operating income of Ethiopian Airlines. The many routes that opium takes to the ultimate consumer of heroin are worldwide. Raw opium is grown in the Far East, the Middle East, and Mexico; it is processed into heroin from Hong Kong to Marseilles; the heroin is delivered to the great ports of the world for distribution down to the lowly "hophead" in the dingy alleys of the larger cities. The profits flow centripetally into the strongboxes of organized crime rings, with the overflow going into numbered bank accounts in Switzerland. Alcohol is displacing some of the more traditional agents—for example, kava in Polynesia and the betel nut in the East Indies. Now that rapid transportation has brought an assortment of psychochemicals to the local black marketplace, price and preference become the major factors, rather than local availability. The novelty of the drug is very important, as we shall see.

We have gone through cycles of intense drug misuse before. All classes of mind alterers have had their periods of popularity and decline. As one strolls past Needle Park in New York, Haight-Ashbury in San Francisco, or Capsule Corner in Los Angeles, it may appear that a new phenomenon is being observed. This is hardly true. Nor is it necessary to reach back to the bacchanalian orgies of Rome, the penny gin of seventeenth-century London, the widespread addiction which attended the opium wars, or the multitudes of Middle Eastern hashish eaters. Just one century ago in the English-speaking countries a flood of drugs was unleashed. It will be instructive to look at that scene briefly so that a more balanced view of our present situation may be achieved.

Just after the Civil War, more distilled spirits were being consumed per capita than today. This occurred despite a vigorous temperance movement. Many of the devout temperance advocates themselves felt no qualms in taking a warming nip of some patent medicine—for example, Hostetter's Bitters, 47 percent alcohol by volume. It is fascinating that no less a psychologist-philosopher than William James wrote in his *Varieties of Religious Experience*, "The sway of alcohol over mankind is unquestionably due to its power to stimulate the mystical faculties of human nature usually crushed to earth by the cold facts and dry criticisms of the sober hour." Our latter-day chemical mystics call alcohol a "downer," and no one even pretends to drink whiskey for its mystical qualities these days.

In England opium usage was really serious. Rich and poor, poet and peasant, all could buy laudanum (tincture of opium) or gum opium from any apothecary. "Happiness might now be bought for a penny and carried in the waistcoat pocket. Portable ecstasies might be had in a bottle, and peace of mind sent down by the mail," wrote Thomas De Quincey in his *Confessions of an English Opium Eater*. The lyric descriptions of the heavenly mind-releasing effects of opium are strangely reminiscent of the psychedelic narrations of today.

Chloroform and ether were novelties during the nineteenth century. The public was fascinated by these strange, pungent liquids and managed to find ways to misuse them. At Cambridge University chloroform parties were enjoyed for a while, until its toxicity became apparent. The safer ether was more widely used for ether frolics at Harvard and other centers of learning where adventurous young people gathered. These revels took place even before the anesthetic potential of ether was known. But it was not sniffed merely for a cheap drunk. William James, that nineteenth-century arbiter of the religious experience, called it "a stimulator of the mystical consciousness." Ether is now considered a mundane anesthetic; when it first appeared, it was a highly regarded consciousness expander.

Nitrous oxide, commonly called laughing gas, must be adjudged the primary nineteenth-century psychedelic. Sir Humphry Davy discovered that it could disinhibit in the most delightful and hilarious manner. Many artists and students inhaled it for its voluptuous sensations and entrancing chromatic fantasies. Visions of Paradise, universal truths, and enormous insights were all experienced and duly reported. On college campuses and at certain dinner parties, laughing gas was the fashionable, the only genteel way to become "potted," to lose one's inhibitions. At sideshows and county fairs nitrous oxide inhalations were dispensed for a quarter. Some customers went on a laughing jag; others discovered final truths. A few met with nothing but a sick stomach and dizziness for their two bits. How interesting that we are beginning to hear about laughing gas abuse again now, a hundred years later.

Unless we learn from it, we are condemned to repeat history. Dismal repetitions of the drug-taking errors of the past are once more under way, with agents much more powerful and diverse and just as incompletely understood.

It took thousands of years to recognize the harm that excessive drinking could do—for example, that alcohol predisposed to cirrhosis of the liver. For centuries opium was not known to be addictive. Dozens of years had to pass before the Western world recognized cocaine as a dangerous agent. The long latent period which lies between the start of widespread misuse of a drug and the full recognition of its harmful effects is an old story. Of the agents now in vogue, many are known to be harmful, some are claimed to be safe. Regarding the safety of the latter, it may be prudent to consider the old claims of safety for alcohol, opium, and cocaine.

It has been said that ours is a drug-taking age. Perhaps we are not entitled to that distinction when we glance back at earlier times. Those who speak of this as an age of drugs seem to justify their misuse on the grounds that others are using antibiotics, tranquilizers, or antidepressants—but in proper amounts and for proper reasons. This is a strange logic. Perhaps this period is better called the age of miracles. Daily we witness the miraculous cures of medicine and the miracles of science and technology. Why should we not expect a miracle pill to cure us of our hurts, provide instant happiness, instant maturity, and instant love?

Many of the drugs which dissociate the self, thought, emotion, and sensation, call them hallucinogenic or psychedelic, have been around for a long time. It is the novelty of each new chemical that makes it singularly attractive. The dissociated state can be obtained by a wide variety of agents in addition to those we ordinarily classify as psychedelic. I have already mentioned anesthetics, narcotics, stimulants, and deliriants that have been called procurers of the mystical experience.

Controls over the abuse of chemicals are necessary, but simply passing laws is rarely a final solution. The abuse of alcohol was not solved by the Volstead Prohibition Act; indeed, it bred crime and provoked disrespect for the law. More successful, but hardly curative, was the Harrison Narcotics Act, which reduced the number of cocaine and opiate users but created a criminal hierarchy supported by those locked into heroin. The Pure Food and Drug laws successfully swept unstandardized, mislabeled, and falsely advertised nostrums from the shelves of the grocer and druggist. Why the varying degrees of success of the three laws? The amount of public support is one part of the answer. Whether the substance is culture-alien or culturally accepted is another. The third part of the answer involves a major task of our day. It is to teach the young how to live in a changing world and how to establish new goals when the old ones become threadbare and irrelevant.

We perennially forget the cyclic nature of a man's development. A young person is more curious, less cautious, more impulsive, more willing to take a chance, and certainly more idealistic. Many youths are fascinated by mind-changing drugs, especially the new ones. Their elders are appalled by the dangerous exploration of insufficiently studied chemicals. As the young grow and mature, they tend to withdraw from the chemical roulette. When they become parents, they are dismayed in turn by the goings-on of their children. The generation gap is the distance between the parents' forgetting and their childrens' not knowing.

SOME DEFINITIONS

This book will concentrate on the more reasonable concept of drug dependence rather than of habituation or addiction, although these concepts are not completely abandoned. *Drug dependence* is a state of psychic or physical dependence, or both, arising in a person following administration of a drug on a periodic or continuous basis. But drug dependence is of a highly variable nature, and to be accurate it is necessary to state the kind of dependence. The World Health Organization classifies the following major types of drug dependence:

1 The morphine type
2 The barbiturate-alcohol type
3 The cocaine type
4 The Cannabis (marihuana) type
5 The amphetamine type
6 The khat type
7 The hallucinogen (LSD) type

For those who wish to retain the concepts of addiction and habituation, their official definitions are included. *Drug addiction* is a state caused by periodic or chronic intoxication produced by the repeated consumption of a natural or synthetic drug. Its characteristics include: 1 an overpowering desire or need (compulsion) to continue taking the drug and to obtain it by any means; 2 a tendency to increase the dose (tolerance); 3 a psychic and generally a physical dependence; 4 detrimental effects on the individual or on society. *Drug habituation* is a condition resulting from the repeated consumption of a drug. Its characteristics include: 1 a desire, but not a compulsion, to continue taking the drug for the sense of improved well-being which it engenders; 2 some degree of psychic dependence on the effect of the drug, but absence of physical dependence (and hence of an abstinence syndrome); 3 detrimental effects, if any, primarily on the individual.

Tolerance is the ability of the organism to become used to increasing amounts of an agent. Therefore, to achieve an equivalent psychic effect, larger and larger doses are needed. Eventually, a quantity which would be lethal in a nontolerant individual can be taken without danger. *Cross-tolerance* is the phenomenon whereby one drug is taken and tolerance to another is developed. Heroin produces cross-tolerance to morphine, and cross-tolerance to LSD can be accomplished with mescaline.

If an animal or person is tolerant to a drug and it is suddenly discontinued, an *abstinence syndrome* may appear. Presumably, the body cells not only have accepted the drug but have so altered their metabolism that they now require its presence. A substantial heroin habit is known to produce serious withdrawal effects. An excellent example of the abstinence syndrome is the delirium tremens which begins about 8 to 12 hours after abstaining from long-term alcohol or barbiturate usage. Convulsions, tremors, and delirium are some of the withdrawal effects. On

Skid Row these are commonly known as the "rum fits," the "shakes," and the "horrors."

It is interesting how many pharmacological classes of drugs are capable of abuse. At one end of the scale are *anesthetics,* such as ether, alcohol, and laughing gas. They produce relaxation, excitation (as a disinhibiting effect), and finally coma. The pain-assuaging *narcotics* include opium and its derivatives—morphine, codeine, Dilaudid, and heroin. Related synthetic preparations like Demerol, methadone, and Percodan are also pain relievers, euphoriants, and, in large amounts, producers of hallucinations or unconsciousness. Next in order are *sedatives* like the barbiturates, which quiet, relax, and eventually induce sleep. The tranquilizers, for example, Miltown, are sedatives which calm without inducing excessive drowsiness. On the other side of the mood scale are the *stimulants,* which elevate one's spirits, alert, and, in large doses, excite. They are exemplified by the amphetamines. The *hallucinogens,* or *psychedelics,* are capable of producing perceptual alterations up to hallucinations, intense emotional changes of wide variations, a nonrational, reverie type of thinking, and ego distortions such as loss of self and feelings of complete strangeness. This group is typified by LSD. The *deliriants* induce more mental confusion than the hallucinogens but are just as capable of providing hallucinations, delusions, and changes of emotionality and of the self. A common example would be belladonna or Jimson weed. Actually, every group mentioned can intoxicate, that is, produce a delirium. It is evident, then, that although many classes of drugs invoke mental changes, the overlap is considerable.

The symptoms of the mind-changing drugs may require defining. *Illusions* are misinterpretations of a sensation, e.g., a stain on a wall seen as a face. *Hallucinations* are projections onto the environment for which no sensory cue exists, e.g., hearing voices or seeing objects which others are unable to sense. *Delusions* are erroneous beliefs which are not amenable to reason. *Paranoid* refers to incorrect persecutory or grandiose ideas; *paranoia* would be a fixed ideational system preoccupied with the erroneous ideas. *Mania* includes a flight of ideas, overactivity, and distractibility.

Drug abuse is worth defining. It is the persistent and usually excessive self-administration of any drug which has resulted in psychological or physical dependence or which deviates from approved social patterns of the culture.

THE PSYCHEDELICS ... LSD & OTHERS

CHAPTER THREE

The psychedelics (also called hallucinogens, psychotomimetics, mysticomimetics, and phantastica) are a diverse group of drugs which alter mood, perception, thinking, and ego structure. In small doses they tend to be euphoriant and do not cloud consciousness. In larger amounts a spectrum of reaction forms is possible, ranging from horror to ecstasy, from absence of thought to a manicky flight of ideas, from intensification of color and depth to illusions and hallucinations, and from minor distortions of the body image to complete loss of ego boundaries.

The varieties of psychedelic experiences can best be understood when it is recognized that the intrinsic character structure of the individual is but one of many variables that determine the nature of the "trip." In a situation where the censoring function of the rational mind is obliterated, it is not surprising that environmental states or one's expectations will strongly alter the ensuing experience. It is, then, a condition of extreme suggestibility where minor cues come to assume enormous significance and great mood swings can be precipitated by hitherto insignificant stimuli.

CLASSIFICATION

A classification of the more common hallucinogens would include:

1 *Those containing an indole nucleus*

    a Lysergic acid diethylamide (LSD), a semisynthetic from the fungus ergot (*Claviceps purpurea*). Other lysergic acid variants include lysergic acid amide and lysergic acid hydroxyethylamide, found in at least four species of the tropical American morning glory.

    b Dimethyltryptamine (DMT) and its analogues.

    c Bufotenine, found along with DMT in small quantities in the skin of the toad *Bufo marines*.

    d Psilocybin and psilocin, from mushrooms (*Psilocybe mexicana* and related varieties).

    e Ibogaine, found in the bean and root of the African vine *Tabernanthe iboga*.

    f Harmine, found in caapi (also called yage and ayahuasca).

2 *Those containing a phenyl ring*

    a Mescaline, found in the buttons of the peyote cactus *Lophophora williamsii*. It is 3,4,5-trimethoxy-phenylethylamine.

    b STP. It is 2,5-dimethoxy-4-methyl-amphetamine, a synthetic.

    c Tetrahydrocannabinols, found in the flowering tops and leaves of Indian hemp (*Cannabis sativa*).

    d Anticholinergic hallucinogens. Ditran, Sernyl, and similar synthetics.

LYSERGIC ACID DIETHYLAMIDE (LSD)

Of the psychedelics the most potent and best-studied is LSD. It will be considered the prototype of the hallucinogens, although mention will be made of the others. It was synthesized in 1938 by Hofmann, who accidentally discovered its profound psychic properties five years later. He apparently inhaled enough to induce marked and strange symptoms. It is also active when swallowed or injected.

Physiological and psychological effects

LSD is probably the most powerful drug known; 25 mcg (micrograms) will produce a mild effect in most people. This amount is almost invisible to the naked eye. Doses of about 100 mcg orally are considered average. After such an amount is taken, nothing is noticed for 20 to 120 minutes; then the symptoms increase in an undulating fashion to a peak 2 to 3 hours after ingestion. Thereafter, a phasic waning of the drug's activity occurs, and in 8 to 12 hours recovery is usually complete. To understand the minimal amounts required, it should be noted that 1 oz. will supply about 280,000 doses of 100 mcg each. When larger amounts are used, a few hundred to a few thousand mcg, the experience is intensified and prolonged. The lethal dose for human beings is not precisely known, but it may be approximately 15,000 mcg.

Tolerance develops rapidly if the same dose of LSD is taken daily. Its effect decreases so that practically nothing will be noticed on the fourth day. Cross-tolerance to mescaline and psilocybin has also been demonstrated, indicating that they probably act over cerebral mechanisms similar to LSD. Tolerance is also lost rapidly, usually within 48 hours.

True physical addiction does not occur, in that abstinence effects do not follow abrupt withdrawal. Dependence on the psychic aspects of the LSD state is well known. Stimulants or other psychedelics potentiate LSD activity; sedatives and tranquilizers counteract it. A delicate chromatographic test is now available to detect small amounts of LSD in blood, urine, and spinal fluid.

The single most notable physical sign of LSD action is dilated pupils which do not contract completely when illuminated. Nausea, more rarely vomiting, and chilliness and tremulousness are sometimes seen. Aside from a rare convulsion, the serious physical side effects are minimal.

The psychic aspects of the drug will be briefly described. One of the first noticed signs is a colorful pattern of geometric or other symmetrical designs moving across the visual field when the eyes are closed. Later, these may become complex events, persons, or symbolic fantasies. With open eyes, colors become more saturated, depth is accentuated, and the afterimage is prolonged. Fixed stationary objects may move, and other illusions are seen. Visual hallucinations—seeing things that are not visible to others —are less frequent. Generally, subjects report that the viewed object has enhanced beauty and meaning, but the opposite has also been described. Hearing seems intensified, with background noise coming into awareness; taste, smell, and touch are variably altered. The sense of time may be enormously slowed. Euphoria is common, and ecstatic states are described. From 10 to 15 percent of the experiences are panicky and quite frightening. Thought is fantasy-laden, and rational, logical thought is lost at the higher doses. The ego may fragment, the concept of one's body can alter greatly, and in ultimate states complete loss of the idea of self takes place.

It is evident that if these striking changes develop in a context of fear and disorganization, a psychosis intervenes. This is the "bum trip," or "freakout"—what was called a "model psychosis" in the earlier years of LSD investigation. Horrifying experiences also result from fear that one is going to be permanently insane or that one may die. They also occur when personal repressed memories are resurrected which overwhelm the individual. A bad trip is not considered a complication if restitution of the individual is complete when the drug has worn off. Complications are more likely to follow a fear-ridden experience, but they are known to occur after highly pleasurable experiences as well.

Motivation to take LSD

Before considering the possible untoward events that can occur, something must be said about the kinds of LSD takers and their reasons for taking the drug. Since 1962 the drug has been available in nonmedical channels. A substantial number of people have known the drug experience. Who are they?

As numerous as any group are the inquisitive, those who are willing to take the chance of swallowing a strange chemical with unusual effects. Their curiosity may range from a desire for new experience to a professional interest in the strange mental processes that intervene. Ordinarily, these are people who take LSD once or a very few times are satisfied with the event, and have no particular interest in pursuing the matter.

At the other extreme are the serious "acidheads," who by now have consumed LSD in a startling range of doses, hundreds of times, in a few cases more than a thousand times. A few individuals have allegedly consumed over a million "mikes." To accomplish this, other activities—educational or vocational—must be subordinated or set aside, for taking the drug even once or twice a week precludes most unassociated activities. In addition, routine life games become increasingly unattractive, and withdrawal from society is not uncommon. The withdrawal is usually into a similarly oriented subgroup whose members reinforce each other's beliefs and play an important role in maintaining the asocial posture. The most frequent reason given for adopting the LSD way of life is that it opens a religious vista or fulfills a sense of meaning in existence. The retreat is expressed as a disillusion with the injustices, the insanities, the superficialities of Western existence and an escape from this incurable and intolerable way of life. The threat of instant annihilation via impending atomic warfare is frequently stated as a reason why any effort to correct or alter the evils of existence is futile. Many of these people are attracted or introduced to contrived versions of the Eastern mystical religions. The so-called universal insights of the LSD state can be neatly fitted into their open-ended generalities. This is an attempt to return to spiritual nature at a time when the stresses and strains, complexities, and obscure goals of existence are difficult to endure. It is the spiritual equivalent of the French nobility at the time of Louis XVI putting on peasant costumes so that they could participate in Rousseau's call for a return to nature.

Very substantial numbers of LSD users are "high" seekers. This is often openly stated without pretense at deeper, more significant motivations. At times a rationalization to cover up the hedonistic use of the drug is made. More ostensibly profound reasons, for example, that the drug experience is for learning about oneself or one's relationship with life, are proffered. The intense preoccupation with ways to avoid bum trips indicates that pleasure seeking is a major reason for LSD usage. Actually, the bum trip could be a more meaningful and educational event than the good one, for at last the old terrors could be looked at and worked through. If pleasure were not a frequent component of the LSD state, it would never have achieved its current level of popularity. Another indication that the kick's the thing is the addition of amphetamines to the LSD potion. Especially in the very young group of LSD users, the reason for the addition is explicitly or implicitly the same, "It's a high." Those who cannot enjoy without chemicals, those whose life situation is dismal, those who

have a low tolerance for assumed or actual difficult lives, those who will try anything—these are the high seekers.

Social pressures are brought to bear on the youngster who finds himself in the company of acidheads. To be a "square" is to be, in some circles, a social leper. The persuasion may be direct or indirect, the latter consisting in the pain of being outside an "in" group. The natural tendency of the young to imitate peer behavior is especially strong in forbidden rites. Epidemics of LSD taking have been observed in schools when a small group has gained status by indulging in the new fad. Its members proceed to demonstrate their special powers by initiating their classmates. This sort of "turning on" everyone can be especially disastrous to the young person who has internal reservations about taking the drug but whose peers talk about nothing else. These reservations may stem from an appropriate inner knowledge that LSD is not for him. I know of instances where the LSD casualty did not want to try the drug, but his friends insisted. A strong philosophic position must be provided to prevent this form of social arm twisting from taking its toll of reluctant LSD candidates. The choice is not one of being "hip" or "square." Other options are possible: Nonchemical forms of temporary detachment are available and tend to be more valid.

Artists and quasi artists have always been nonconformists. In earlier days they explored all sorts of chemicals in the hope that they might get outside themselves. They hope somehow to break through their ordinary frame of reference and see anew, to compose the dissonance about them. The artist is perpetually concerned about access to his creative sources, and when he enters a cyclic period of infertility, he searches for devices to release the Muse. It is not surprising, therefore, that some artists and some arty sets have embraced the psychedelics. Whether psychedelic art has any merit must be judged by those qualified. Regarding creativity, it must be remembered that drive and hard work are

the essentials, and these are more often diminished than enhanced by repetitive LSD usage. Inspiration, which is too often
mistaken for creativity, can occur under the influence of LSD.
Inspiration is but a fragment of the total creative process. Bach
said, "Anyone can write my concertos, if he would work as hard
as I." Unfortunately, the feeling of having achieved an original
solution often exceeds the proof. In one study investigating this
matter, the subjective impression that one had become more
creative as a result of LSD taken under optimal conditions could
not be confirmed objectively, using the best available tests of
artistic or ideational creativity. LSD subjects, given 200 mcg
under optimal conditions three times, did no better than the
matched control group six months after their last session.

Sufficient LSD is around so that occasionally individuals will in-
gest some unknowingly. This is particularly true of children, who
are notorious oral characters. They have a penchant for the
LSD-saturated sugar cube but will swallow any capsule, tablet, or
liquid in their path. Adults are also known who have put what
they thought was plain sugar in their coffee and gone on extended
"journeys." These experiences are usually as unhappy as those
"trips" taken by people who have been purposely introduced to
LSD without their knowledge. Its deliberate administration to
a victim for fun or with other than friendly intent is known.
This is a particularly mindless and vicious practice. When the
room is swirling, time standing still, and thinking awry, it is very
comforting to recall that one has taken a drug which induced the
strange condition. This knowledge is denied the person who
develops LSD effects without knowing what caused them. The
experience is generally horrifying, and such tricks have been known
to end in suicide or psychosis.

In one investigation into the possible effects of prolonged high-
dosage LSD intake on brain damage, surprisingly very few subjects could be found who used only that drug. Almost all had
tried other psychedelics. Marihuana was invariably smoked. In

addition, experimentation with a wide variety of other substances, many of them mentioned in other chapters of this book, was mentioned. "Uppers" and "downers," airplane glue and nutmeg —these and many other nonpsychedelics were consumed in a sort of chemical smorgasbord fashion. Although it was rare, heroin was mentioned; the use of some brand of codeine cough syrup was less uncommon. Even cocaine was "joy-popped" by 3 of the 30 subjects. The pure acidhead exists and frowns on this psychochemical potpourri, but he is the exception. It was found that drug-taking behavior tends to spread to other classes of pharmaceuticals. Grab-bag parties where any one of a variety of drugs may be chosen by chance are known. What remains unknown is the mentality of the gambler.

The user of psychedelics is unique in claiming a religious or self-searching motive for his drug activities. Despite the fact that opiates, anesthetics, and other classes of drugs can cause similar experiences, no "hophead" or "pillhead" makes a particular virtue out of his habit. Unfortunately, only a small minority of psychedelic users actually search for meaning via LSD. If all LSD experiences were horrifying but meaningful, the LSD problem would cease to be a problem. Further, if LSD is a sacrament, why the need for adding narcotics, barbiturates, and amphetamines?

It was also of interest in this investigation to estimate whether the fervent LSD taker had stopped smoking tobacco or drinking alcohol. The claim is made that these unhealthy practices are often eliminated as a result of LSD experiences. In fact, one of the major hopes of researchers into the potential of LSD is that it may alter a destructive drinking pattern. It was found that only a few individuals had reduced or discontinued their tobacco or whiskey consumption. Of course, this finding has no bearing on the issue of the role of LSD in treating problem alcoholics. Special techniques are necessary when the drug is used for alcoholism. LSD alone is rarely sufficient to do the job.

It has also been said that the psychedelics are the younger generation's grog. Perhaps this is true in a few instances, but the frequency of alcohol usage among psychedelicists does not seem to
indicate a sharp break with the more traditional mind changers.

It is by no means invariable that a horrendous "freakout" or a
prolonged adverse reaction will cause the person to remain absti-
nent. I am sometimes asked whether LSD might not help get
a person out of a complication that LSD had precipitated. This
reflects the magical thinking of the drug taker. It should not be
surprising that one or a series of "freakouts" or "flipouts" does not
induce a person to abstain.

It is interesting, and perhaps indicative of a trend, that a few of
the avid and devout acidheads, some from the original Leary-led
group, have given up LSD. When queried, they state that they
eventually realized that LSD "could not do it," that LSD was leading them down to a dead end, or that they finally recognized that
they were functioning ineffectively. Others who have quit have
said, "LSD taught me something, but I have to do the rest myself."

On the other hand, rather large numbers of people have adopted
the LSD way of life. They have heeded the siren call to "drop
out." These are, perhaps, the saddest of the LSD casualties, for
they are hung up on illusory notions. One is that the transcendental experience, however obtained, is the end, when in fact it is but
the beginning. Another is that being is better than becoming.
Still another is that the insights gained under LSD are inevitably
valid.

The hip culture is essentially a psychedelic drug culture. It would
be incorrect to think of the members as a homogeneous group.
They range from the phoniest to the most dedicated, from the
schizophrenic girl who runs away into the subculture that accepts
her weirdness to the genius at odds with society. The LSD drop-

out naturally gravitates toward the hip colony, which has more than its share of "losers"—those who cannot enjoy without chemicals and those with a low tolerance for frustration.

As might be predicted, the people who should avoid exposure to a potent mind-shaking chemical like LSD are often the very ones attracted to it. They hope, via the magic of this spectacular experience, to be cured of their failings. The schizoid hopes to come into more meaningful contact with others. The immature seek easy instant maturity. The confused yearn for clarity. To the alienated, the ambulatory psychotic, the distraught, and the dependent, LSD seems to provide the answer. It is these very people that are high-risk candidates for psychedelics. They are more apt to get into serious difficulties because they do not have the stability to sustain them. Nor is a joyous maiden LSD voyage proof that one has passed "the acid test." The personal encounter can be skirted by a variety of techniques; but even after dozens of trips, the fragile vessel may sink on a subsequent one. The emotionally immature or unstable, the paranoid and the hysterical personalities, the prepsychotic, and those with very rigid belief systems would be excluded from any serious research study. Under nonmedical conditions, no attempt is made to sort them out. Very depressed individuals should never be given LSD except under the most protected conditions. Even the stable person may get into difficulty with LSD on occasion, especially when the circumstances are poor or he is unprotected. Therefore everybody should not turn on as some devotees still proclaim. If the present trend continues, with larger amounts of LSD being consumed more and more by younger and younger people, the possibilities of adverse reactions will increase. The preteen-ager does not have the emotional resilience to withstand the enormity of some LSD experiences, and he can be swept off his fragile emotional foundations. Age, of course, is no guarantee. Every susceptible category mentioned above is represented in the adult population. However, the life style of a few adults has been a suitable preparation for the psychedelic experience, and they handle it well.

Significance of the LSD state

The psychedelic boom must mesh with the spirit of our times. After all, hashish, the extract of *Cannabis indica,* was on drugstore shelves for over a century, and it was all but ignored. The plant itself grew wild in many parts of the United States, but it attracted few smokers. Peyote was readily purchasable through the mail, but with comparatively few takers. Havelock Ellis predicted a great future for mescaline at the turn of the century, but it never did become popular. Apparently, the drug-taking taboo (with certain exceptions) was strong enough to keep all but the most deculturated away. Now that most taboos are either dissolved or in process of dissolution, drug usage becomes acceptable, even fashionable. When this breakdown of tribal proscriptions occurs in the context of alienation and absence of goals, a drug like LSD provides feelings of union and meaningfulness. Disbelief yields to belief. Psychic pain is assuaged, and dysphoria becomes euphoria.

Although ours is not the most stressful of eras, it is the most rapidly changing. The cultural limits become indistinct. Chemical faith and pharmacological happiness are widely available. The magic of the new, mysterious, miraculous pill attracts. Admittedly psychopaths and inadequates have always sought out any manner of providing oblivion, but the psychedelics attract, among others, those of little faith and those who cannot endure their sober life.

The good LSD trips can banish tension and provide pleasure. Like alcohol, LSD (and to a lesser degree marihuana) is claimed to enhance the sex act. Like alcohol, LSD is not an aphrodisiac but a disinhibitor; it permits loosening of strict superego controls. Because of this, sexual activities may be indulged in more readily. The heightened sensory awareness and the prolongation of subjective time may enhance the mental elaboration of the sex act. In one set of experimental subjects, no sexual acting out nor even sexual fantasies occurred. The specific behavior depends upon the implanting of ideas and the presence of erotic stimuli during the drug session.

Since the psychedelics are taken by some to provide insightful mystical states, we must ask: 1 whether the insights are valid, and 2 whether the chemical mystical state is the same as the mystical state that comes naturally or is induced by arduous training. The validity of what is seen under a drug like LSD varies greatly. Some flashes of inspired awareness are obviously delusional, and acting upon them can be devastating. Information that comes to the LSD user seems more real than ordinary reality. This does not mean that it is. It may simply mean that he is unable to discriminate and to sort out the exceedingly convincing notions that come to him. He is in a completely credulous, vulnerable state, without the ability to critically examine his thoughts. Some of the ideas may have merit; they should be carefully scrutinized in the days that follow an LSD experience. The world of psychedelia exists in our fantasy; its truthfulness has approximately the same validity as our dreams. Much of it is chaff, but the wheat kernels should be examined closely, for it emanates from our own unconscious and may have revealing things to tell us.

One of the notable aspects of the thinking process of the habitual LSD user is his credulousness. This quality of believing anything and everything extends into the sober period. He is so loosened up that little is scrutinized and all sorts of oddities are accepted. Astrology, palmistry, and other medieval superstitions are incorporated without particular discrimination. This looseness of judgment should not be confused with the vagueness and confusion of perennial acidheads, who could have sustained brain-cell deficits as a result of their protracted use of dubious supplies of LSD. The willingness to believe anything is harmless unless it results in overt behavior sufficiently inappropriate, discordant, and odd.

Legal and logistic problems

In 1966 a federal law making the manufacture, transportation, giving away, or sale of LSD and other psychedelics felonious was
enacted.   Various states and cities have statutes making possession
and usage either a misdemeanor or a felony.   The nature of felonies is not well understood by the young people who commit
them.   This is unfortunate, for they should be aware of the serious-
ness of a conviction on a felony charge.   It involves not only a jail
sentence, but it includes loss of civil rights and can be a bar to
many vocations and professions.

The supply of LSD has not appreciably decreased.   It is still being
made in clandestine garages, chemistry laboratories, and kitchens
in this country, and it is being brought across the national boundaries.   The smuggling of LSD is easy because it is so powerful
that an enormous amount can be carried in an envelope or dissolved onto pieces of blotting paper.   In addition, it has no odor
and is not easy to detect by chemical means.   Supplies of LSD
make their way down to the final consumer through a series of
large-scale and small-scale pushers.   The latter are often acidheads
making their living by selling the solution, capsule, tablet, or sugar
cube.   At one time it was not unusual to be given LSD free as a
gesture of friendship, but that is much rarer now.   In one or two
cities organized criminals have moved in on the lucrative LSD
trade.

The quality of the black-market material varies widely.   Some
LSD is almost pure.   Some samples have been found to contain
a little LSD and many other products which could not be identified.   The alleged amount of LSD in any single dose is rarely accurate.   A 250-mcg capsule may have as little as 50 mcg of LSD;
less frequently it contains much more.   At least one manufacturer puts Methedrine and 100 mcg of LSD into capsules which
he peddles as containing 300 mcg.   The result of these manipula-

tions by the manufacturer or pusher who "cuts the cap" means that no faith whatsoever should be placed in allegations of the amount in each dose. People who claim to have taken 10,000 mcg may have swallowed one-tenth as much. One rumor in southern California that the LSD was being adulterated with heroin to get people "hooked" was found to be untrue on analysis of the substance. Coloring material is sometimes added, but the various colors have no significance.

Uses

One of the tragic aspects of the current LSD scene is the decrease in orderly research with this drug. It is not that research has been discouraged, but that it has become much more difficult to perform. Some capable investigators either have been denied the drug or have withdrawn from active involvement. With public attitudes toward LSD so polarized, it is hardly possible to obtain subjects without a preconceived bias about what will happen to them. As we have seen, a preconception can markedly alter the drug state.

LSD has been of real value in stimulating research and providing information on the nature of the chemistry of the brain. This basic knowledge is valuable and may have important impact in practical applications in the coming years.

The possibility of using LSD as a psychotherapeutic device has intrigued some psychiatrists for many years. A number of European therapists are using the drug in small doses to reduce defensiveness, increase emotional response to the recall of repressed material and to aid in its retrieval from the unconscious. In North America a few studies are under way employing the chemical transcendental state as a way to provide a sort of psychological death-rebirth experience. It could be a new beginning for those who have been living a self-destructive kind of existence. The technique has been used with chronic alcoholics, drug addicts, and persons with similar disorders. The earlier studies were quite promising. Now the controlled studies are under way, and the final results are not in. In the first two controlled studies to be reported, the LSD group did no better than the control group after a follow-up of one year. The follow-up period, so necessary for evaluating whether a sustained change in the individual's way of life has really taken place, is still under way in six other investigations.

Some encouraging results have been found in a number of cases of infantile autism, a condition in which the child makes little or no contact with his environment. However, this may not be due to the psychic activity of LSD, since methysergide, an LSD analogue without its psychedelic effects, also improves the autistic child.

Research indicates that LSD may have a role to play in the treatment of certain patients who are having difficulty accepting their imminent death. It has been used predominantly in patients with terminal cancer who are in anguish about their death. It should be reserved for those who are not helped by other measures. In such selected instances it has been found to be of benefit to about half the patients to whom it has been given. What happens is that during the "out of the body" state, a change in values can be induced. This change can consist in instilling in this patient a sense of meaning in his personal existence and a feeling that since there is meaning in life, there is meaning in death. Those patients who seemed benefited felt calmer about their oncoming demise, often required less narcotics, and were able to make their final emotional peace with their families.

Complications

The physical aftereffects are not noteworthy. A very rare case of cardiovascular collapse or of a major convulsion has been seen. Human deaths directly due to LSD poisoning are not known.

We are aware that in animal and in a few human studies brain-wave changes and certain learning abilities were altered for weeks, sometimes months, after an exposure to LSD. These reports are too tentative to lead to firm conclusions. In the matter of chromosomal changes, too, the implications are not yet evident. The possibility that any alteration in chromosomal structure is innocuous is not great. These cellular structures produce protein messages of ribonucleic acid (RNA) which instruct the cell what to manufacture. Structural change usually reflects functional change, but the nature of that change is not manifest at this time. In some preliminary studies using the white blood cells of high-dose LSD takers, definite abnormalities in chromosomal structure have been found. Infants born of mothers who have taken LSD during pregnancy show similar fragmentation and transposition of chromosomal material. Five rats were given a single dose of LSD early in pregnancy, equivalent by weight to the amounts taken by human beings on the street. Three of them aborted or had stillborn litters. A fourth delivered 1 runted and 7 healthy offspring. The fifth rat delivered a normal litter. The five control rats, given placebo injections, all delivered healthy litters of 11 to 16 offspring. Are the chromosomal changes temporary or permanent? What disease may become manifest? Until these and other questions are answered, it may be prudent for those who are of childbearing age or below to avoid exposure to LSD. Unfortunately, it may be years before a definite answer to these questions will become available.

The meaning of these and other studies are not clear. It is well known that years must elapse before some genetic alterations become manifest. Sometimes an environmental factor is needed to permit the defect to become evident. It is certain that if these changes are seen in white blood cells, they also occur in other body cells. White blood cells are routinely used in cytogenetic studies because they are the most readily available cells.

It may be well to review the evidence that has appeared in a dozen articles, recognizing that many other studies are under way. It is hoped that a more definite statement can be made in the not too distant future. Every experiment but one has demonstrated that breaks or transposition of chromosomal material occurs three or four times more frequently in LSD users than in nonusers. The size of the dose of LSD is roughly related to the presence of the abnormalities. Similar alterations in the leukocytes (white blood cells) are manifest when they are placed in dilute solutions of LSD. Presumably, all other body cells are similarly affected, but this point remains to be determined.

In animal studies pregnant rats given amounts of LSD equivalent in body weight to that commonly consumed by human beings had stillborn or runted offspring with occasional litters born apparently normal. Similarly treated mice have been born with cerebral malformations. The evidence for human congenital malformations is much less definite. Since children born of mothers who took LSD during pregnancy can also manifest chromosomal damage, it is known that LSD crosses the placenta. The number of malformed babies born to acidhead mothers remains small. In one instance, however, there appears to be a relationship between the mother's LSD taking and an infant with a malformed and shortened leg, since the drug was taken at precisely the time when the bony structure for the leg was laid down, namely during the seventh week of pregnancy.

The nature of the cellular structural alterations induced by LSD has led expert geneticists to speculate that leukemia or cancer might be the likely disorder resulting from the chromosomal change. The proof of this statement will require time. Many of the LSD anomalies are reminiscent of those caused by deep x-ray therapy, certain viruses, and drugs which are used in the treatment of malignancies.

It would be helpful to know how long the alterations of chromosomal material persist. If we can extrapolate from our knowledge of the x-ray-induced changes, some of the material will revert to normal and some alterations will be permanent. One case has shown chromatid breaks 3½ years after the last exposure to LSD. One 2½-year-old child still shows a high percentage of breaks after a single exposure to LSD while in the uterus. No work has yet been done to determine whether the sperm and egg cells of acid-heads are affected. It is, therefore, not advisable at this time to go as far as Dr. Livingston did in his statement: "Recent studies on the effects of LSD on leukocytes show enormous changes. If similar damage is present in the reproductive cells, and if reports of the widespread use of this drug among college students are true, this one drug has probably caused more mutations than all the atomic explosions thus far."

The new findings of chromosomal defects reflect upon a larger issue. All too often someone says, "So long as I do not harm anyone else, I have the freedom to do to myself what I will." To think that one's own actions do not reverberate upon others is magnificently shortsighted. Who would have thought, when the LSD fad started, that direct damage to one's offspring was a possibility? In other instances, the impact of one's actions on others is less direct but still evident.

These changes also bring up the question of brain-cell damage. This is a difficult matter to settle simply or categorically. Rabbits treated with large doses of LSD demonstrate brain-cell vacuoliza-tion and depletion of the cytoplasm. No autopsy reports on the brains of human beings who have taken frequent large amounts have been reported. On a clinical level, acidheads interviewed who had not taken LSD recently showed recent memory defects, inability to form abstract concepts, vagueness, and confusion. These symptoms are more commonly seen in chronic brain dam-age than in schizophrenia. Because of the resemblance of some chronic LSD mental symptoms to organic brain damage, a study of a group of acidheads has been completed. For purposes of this investigation an acidhead was operationally defined as some-one who had taken LSD at least fifty times in large amounts.

None of the members of the group were obviously impaired. They were matched in age, sex, race, and educational level with an equal number of nondrug users. Both groups were given an extensive battery (Halstead-Reitan) of neuropsychological tests designed to test most aspects of mental functioning. It was found that the LSD group performed as well as the control group except in the area of spatial orientation. In tasks requiring good spatial ability, the LSD group did significantly worse at the 1 percent level of confidence. Within the LSD group itself, those who had taken the most trips produced the lowest scores of intelligence (Raven's test).

The psychological complications encountered have been impressive during the past few years. We do not know how often they occur because the incidence of LSD taking is unknown. Nor do physicians see all the untoward results. One can note dazed and disorganized persons walking the streets of the local hip community apparently not under the influence of drugs at the time. Their strangeness is accepted as part of the scene. It must be remembered that the great bulk of LSD casualties are reported in neither the popular nor the medical press. They are no longer news. Unless something really novel happens, the publication of LSD accidents no longer arouses interest. It is curious that most people are shocked by some preliminary chromosomal findings, while the multitude of severe psychological sequelae that are undeniable are casually accepted. The varieties are so great that only the more common can be mentioned.

During the period of LSD intoxication two undesirable reactions are encountered, the panic state and the acute paranoid reaction. It is obvious that the loss of customary controls which the drug engenders can induce a severe panic in the individual who becomes very fearful. If he acts upon his panic, he can hurt himself or others by his unthinking behavior. Deaths have occurred when such a person has run into the path of a car during an unsupervised or poorly supervised trip. The acute paranoid state develops when the tripper becomes exceedingly suspicious or grandiose and proceeds to act upon his delusions. Suspiciousness can result in mindless running from, or assaulting, the object of one's suspicions. Grandiosity, more common, can culminate in megalomaniac ideas of omniscience and indestructibility. This leads to the all too common efforts to fly by jumping out of the window with outstretched arms. Aside from the associated lethality, these miscalculations of one's powers demonstrate how intense the psychedelic conviction can become. These are often not suicides, but accidents due to delusional misjudgment. Other omnipotent feelings can pervade one's being, such as Messianic beliefs that one can walk upon the waters. These, too, have failed. Devout worshippers of the Sun God have been blinded temporarily by gazing steadily at the sun while their pupils were dilated from LSD. One young man became obsessed with the Biblical pronouncement, "If thine eye offend thee, pluck it out," and proceeded to do just that. Another attempted to castrate himself with partial success. Ordinarily, the paranoid state is harmless unless one acts upon the misconception. The feeling of mastery under LSD may be exceedingly strong—and wrong. Suicides do occur, but these are the result of an overwhelming surge of terrifying unconscious memories which cannot be handled. Self-destruction may also result from the horrendous idea that one will persist in the LSD madness forever. Homicide is a rarity.

It should be noted again that even the uncomplicated bum trip is of great discomfort to the user. It is a most unhappy time for an eight-hour eternity, representative of what in bygone days was a temporary madness which could be studied in research laboratories. If the person comes back reconstituted, the unhappy day is of slight importance. Some users desist after a bad trip, but others do not, hoping that the next voyage will be a happier one.

Recurrences of the LSD experience weeks or months after the last drug intake are well known. They may be momentary or persistent. They are prone to occur under conditions of physical or psychic stress. If they happen under conditions that do not require vigilance and are interpreted as pleasant, no difficulties ensue. On the other hand, if they are perceived as proof that one is going insane, persisting adverse states can result following the recrudescence rather than following the experience itself.

Almost every variant of emotional disorder has been seen in the period following an LSD experience. Perhaps the most common is the chronic anxiety state. Following the drug experience the user remains "shook up," depressed, unable to attend, and with an indefinable tension. Some facets of the LSD state remain, perhaps the time distortion or the mobility of fixed objects. A few persons have insomnia because they are afraid to close their eyes; others have phobias or strange body symptoms. Users may be able to carry on or may be so disabled by their anxiety that they cannot function. They may drop out, not because they want to, but because they must.

The prolonged psychotic reactions which are identified with the LSD state are of major importance, and their course is variable. In some instances recovery is rapid with treatment; other instances seem more resistant than ordinary schizophrenic reactions. LSD can precipitate a latent psychotic into schizophrenia, but even well-constituted personalities are not entirely immune to breakdown. All kinds of schizophrenic reactions have been seen, including catatonic, hebephrenic, and schizo-affective states. Manic states and psychotic depressions also are observed. These mimic their naturally occurring counterparts.

One psychotic state worth mentioning in further detail is chronic paranoia. This is an infrequently encountered condition these days; the only instances that have been seen by me during the past few years were all LSD-precipitated. The acute paranoid reaction has already been mentioned. Chronic paranoia consists in the persistent fixed belief after the LSD day is over that one has seen the Great White Light and has been chosen to save the world. After all LSD effects have worn off, the firm conviction that one has a Messianic message remains. This is felt with such certainty that one's life is drastically altered. The thinking disorder is circumscribed by the ineradicable idea that one is omnipotent. Other areas of thinking activity are reasonable and appropriate. LSD paranoics are not so infrequent. I had two of them in my office on one occasion. The first Messiah was relating his plans to take his followers up into the hills and start a new civilization. I was trying to understand why he should feel compelled to leave his family in order to save mankind. At that point the second Messiah, who was supposed to be waiting outside, strode in. He pointed a long finger at me and declaimed, "I am the Lord, thy God." "All right, fine," I said, but I was really concerned about the confrontation between the two chemical deities. It worked out well, however. The sitting Messiah looked the intruder over, considered the matter, and slowly said, "I will allow you to be God." The response seemed to be the height of divine one-upmanship.

Management

The management of undesirable LSD reactions is varied. When acute panic or paranoid behavior occurs, every effort should be made to "talk down" the out-of-control patient. The hypersuggestibility of the condition should be employed to reassure and calm those caught up in unreasoning ideas. It is to prevent these emergencies that a devoted, skilled, and understanding baby-sitter should be in constant attendance during an LSD trip. Many accidents could have been prevented if this simple requirement had been met. If the acutely disturbed person cannot be quieted or diverted from his paranoid beliefs, chemical measures are available. A fast-acting barbiturate given intravenously or intramuscularly in sufficient dosage will produce sleep. Intramuscular chlorpromazine is usually but not always effective. These sedatives or tranquilizers can also be administered by mouth, but have a delayed onset of action and may be ineffective if the dose is insufficient. Because of the suggestibility, a marked placebo effect can sometimes be noted: A vitamin or other pill given with sufficient positive persuasion is occasionally capable of terminating the state. Getting the distraught person to eat or to focus on a single object may be sufficient to quiet him.

The more prolonged reactions also require support and reassurance that the condition will recede. The fear that one will never recover or that one is going mad dominates some of these states. Anxiety and depression can be managed with appropriate medication. Psychotic breaks following LSD exposure vary greatly in their response to expert treatment. Sometimes they respond well to the antipsychotic drugs; sometimes they are resistant and need extended care. Electroshock treatment is indicated for psychotic depressions, especially where the threat of suicide exists.

The psychotherapy of the confirmed acidhead dropout is difficult and requires special techniques. Only rarely is he motivated to stay in treatment. If he does, he has feelings of superiority to the "square" therapist who has not had vast experiences and insights via LSD. If he comes willingly into the therapeutic situation, the outlook is more favorable. If he is pushed into it by concerned parents, less can be accomplished. Like alcoholics who must hit bottom before changing their life style, some LSDers may have to undergo a series of bum trips with prolonged adverse reactions before making a new start. The therapeutic task is to understand as completely as possible, to establish trust and channels of communication, and to demonstrate the positive values of living this life and accepting social responsibilities, the importance of striving for personal maturation, and the gratification of accomplishment in the area of the patient's desires. Underlying the LSD problem are often a characterological passivity, dependence, and fears of engaging in life and in close relations with people. It was because of these very traits that many became involved in the LSD way of life. The matter of helping them understand and resolve these problems remains.

The LSD experience can be so shaking to the unprepared, unstable person that his hold on everyday living can be shattered. In these days when the social system with its obvious flaws is under attack, the LSD dropout seems to express the prevailing disaffection. Actually, dropping out is one of the saddest of the LSD complications. To do nothing but withdraw from a far from perfect culture is a defeatist solution. Every one of us is needed to right social wrongs—to do our share in reducing cruelty, war, injustice, intolerance, and the rest. But the drug dropout denies social responsibility. It is his personal existence which matters, and if he wants to escape from life games, why not? The point is that one cannot escape some game. One can play the hip game, the Messiah game, the no-game game, or whatever; one is nonetheless playing a game. All the psychedelic games have their roles, rules, costumes, jargon, and Bible—and they seem as contrived as the square games.

The goal is not to escape life's games, but to know them. Then existence becomes more meaningful and less pressing. Those who know the transcendental state of awareness best tell us that it's what's down here that counts. The Zennists insist that what may be learned after achieving self-transcendence must be applied to this life—that satori is a means, not an end. The hope that one can leave this existence and stay in some Nirvana-like state perpetually is the biggest hang-up of all. It is an illusion from which some will never escape. A more hopeful sign, on the other hand, is that some are returning, having recognized the sterile nature of their narcissistic preoccupations.

Some acidheads come to see the futility of the dropout's existence on their own. They speak the language, have been where the dropout has been, and have come out on the other side to discover that *this* existence is the important one. They often make good cotherapists. No doubt a Synanon for acidheads will be formed one day. This would be a logical manner of building a bridge for these people back to a more valuable, meaningful life. Many of their specious arguments are best handled on the level of peer discussion. The counselor or therapist must not fall into the childish error that the hippie does when he generalizes that all "plastic people," or members of the Establishment, are the same. This is just as nonsensical as the idea that all hippies are the same.

Prevention

A pervasive problem is the matter of prevention. How do the parent and the community prevent the youngster from getting involved with LSD and similar drugs? The issue is a larger one than simply drug taking by juveniles. The relative affluence of large segments of society, which deprives the young of the immediate, visible goals of making a living or learning a trade, invites a goalless existence unless new and appropriate aspirations are substituted. When parental objectives are focused on material accumulations and outdoing one's neighbor, the teen-ager sees these activities as shallow. More meaningful ideals, such as service to others, will give the growing youth a worthy example to emulate. Many parents, unwilling or unable to set limits for their children, find that they grow up without a feeling for their responsibilities and the rights of others. Other parents so over-react to the deprivations of their own childhoods that they give their offspring everything for nothing. It is hardly surprising that such children grow up confused and directionless. There are rules to the game of life in every culture, and if the young do not learn them, they are disadvantaged. If since his earliest years, everything has been given to a child without any effort required of him, how can he react to the sudden demands made by school and society?

Then there is the matter of the family's own drug-taking activities. More than one pubescent has said to me, "If my father can get stoned on booze, why can't I do the same with pot or acid?" There are counterarguments to such questions, but they are not very effective. In sum, then, the home situation is the most important aspect of prevention.

Even in households which are ideal for the growing child, he may still imitate the drug taking of his friends or schoolmates. Single or very few exploratory trials of drugs by young people should not be met with horrified overreaction, lest the dialogue between parent and child be broken. What is needed here is a clear discussion of the matter, and if the relationship is a genuinely loving one, the possibilities are good that good sense will prevail.

The responsibility of the school is to make accurate information available in a nonsensational manner without exciting morbid curiosity. Severe condemnatory attitudes or scare tactics are useless or worse. To tell a high school or college student that "LSD will rot your brain" is absurd if he has friends who have taken the drug and do not seem to have been damaged. He proceeds to shut you out because you are obviously a square scaremonger. The facts as they are are impressive enough to make a case for the greatest circumspection or abstinence. The LSD proselytizers, though, must be found and either be convinced to desist or be excluded from the school.

In my contacts with young adults who are seriously involved in LSD taking, I have found that they manifest at least some of the following characteristics: They have a sense of dissatisfaction with themselves and their way of life. If they are students, they speak of poor teaching of trivial material. This charge may or may not be justified. At any rate, it reflects their discontent and frustration. They also have strong feelings of loneliness and are scarcely capable of being closely identified with other people and causes.

The feeling of distance from others is especially keen. It gives them a sense of hopelessness about themselves and about life. They express a good deal of hostility toward the adult world. Some of this, too, may be justified; much of it seems a projection of their own inadequacies, their inability to grow into the world. Their spiritual goallessness and inability to empathize give one the impression that they are emotionally disadvantaged.

It is evident why the psychedelics can be so attractive to these people. The drugs give them a feeling of belonging, of oneness, and of significance. Through them they can flaunt their disdain for the Establishment and find non-Establishment religions and philosophies. The psychedelics have been called "cultogenic" drugs. They produce a desire to join others who have had similar experiences in a new cult. That psychedelic feelings of self-fulfillment and enhanced understanding are often illusory does not matter. While the psychedelic honeymoon lasts, it fulfills many needs.

The search for a safer psychedelic is a chimera. The very qualities desired—loss of ego controls, euphoria, and disappearance of rational thought—are those which make it a danger to some under any condition and a danger to all under some conditions. Certainly, some psychedelics are more toxic than others. *Amanita muscaria*, the fly agaric, is a mushroom never to be taken except in total desperation. The poisonous dose is not much more than the effective dose. With LSD the effective dose is much less than the hypothesized lethal one. Despite this, the casualties mount.

THE PSYCHEDELIC ISSUES

Four areas of philosophic argument are presented by those who see in LSD a final solution to their own and the world's shortcomings. Each will be presented and a counterposition taken.

This discussion may be helpful in dealing with the LSD abuser who claims vast personal gains from the drug.

1 *"LSD shows me the real Reality. It is the final
   enlightenment. The insights I gain are true."*

We have a peculiar and primitive awe for nonsober experience. Like the Eskimo tribes that make the local epileptic the priest, we place a premium on chemical dissociation. Opium supposedly procured the real Reality for some nineteenth-century intellectuals. Chloroform supposedly gave Oliver Wendell Holmes the final secret of the universe, which he scribbled down so that it could be retrieved when he recovered. "The stench of turpentine pervades all" was the insight which he thought would solve Nature's mysteries.

Some of the flashes of insight that come to the LSD user are evidently erroneous. The conviction that one can fly, walk on water, or stop a car by focusing on it—all have been tried and all have failed. In fact, the nature of the psychedelic state is one of enormous suggestibility. It has been found possible to instill any kind of idea into observed LSD takers' heads. The Reality one encounters during the intense LSD reaction is a result of the prior programming of the individual and the conscious or unconscious suggestion of the guide.

Those spiritual leaders who have spent their lives studying and experiencing the transcendental state consider chemical enlightenment a delusion. For example, the Indian mystic Meher Baba has repeatedly spoken out against the value of LSD-derived revelations. Martin Buber can be quoted to this point: "Man may master as he will his situation, to which his surroundings also belong; he may, when it is necessary, exchange it for another; but the fugitive flight out of the calm situation into situationless-ness is no legitimate affair of man. And the true nature of all paradises which man creates for himself by chemical or other means is situationless-ness."

What puzzles those who observe the LSD votaries is why weekly enlightenments are necessary. Why hundreds of enlightenments when a single spontaneous one may last a lifetime? Why does the psychedelic religious experience have so little staying power, so little payoff in improved behavior and good conduct? Why the parasitism upon the existing social system that is despised? "A spiritual experience can only be judged by its effects upon the experiencer," said Ramakrishna. The question is not, "Did he have a psychedelic experience?" but, "What were its effects?"

The chemical mystical state is very much like the spontaneous one—but with some important differences. One difference is that the psychedelic experience often leaves the person with an inflated grandiose notion of himself—of having seen the Light and having the Answer—whereas one who returns from the spontaneous experience will often come back with feelings of awe and humbleness. Other important differences will be mentioned later.

A peculiar notion exists that the chemical transcendental state is something for everybody. This notion is not supported by any mystical religion. Sri Krishna forbids imparting higher knowledge to those not ready for it. This strict attitude is also found in the Upanishads and the Vedas. In Raja Yoga strict discipline and self-purification are the indispensable prerequisites for entering Yoga. Otherwise those unprepared for the higher states will be damaged. Compare these cautions to the casual turning on of anyone these days. And "discipline" is a dirty word among psychedelicists.

2   *"This life is not to be endured and leads only to mass insanity and a game-playing existence."*

This statement has popular appeal because it puts the blame for our own shortcomings outside ourselves. If we look only at the current scene rather than the entire sweep of human existence, our times seem alarming and excruciating. The fact is that most generations have had it immeasurably worse. It is the ignorant, including those who have never bothered to learn how it was to live in the "good old days," who believe that things never were so bad.

The struggle against injustice, intolerance, and inhumanity is a perpetual one. Actually, there is reason to believe that slow, intermittent progress is being made in our transition from *Homo faber*, the cunning toolmaker, to *Homo sapiens*, the sapient man. We are creatures in transition with all the stresses and strains of transitional life.

The outcome is in doubt. If our nerve fails—if enough of us withdraw into a chemical oblivion—then we shall fall back into another Dark Age. The Golden Age of Greece, the Renaissance, the Scientific Revolution—these are peaks in man's cyclic effort to approach his destiny. But he has slipped back again and again into the Dark Ages and the Middle Ages of ignorance and superstition.

The dropout's way is certainly not the way. The Zennists recognized the self-defeating nature of passivity. The first rule of Ch'an monastic life was, "A day of no work is a day of no eating." Nor does anything written in Tantric, Zennist, or other Buddhist literature condone promiscuity, indolence, or anarchy. Discipline is constantly referred to as the way to freedom and spontaneity.

What seems infinitely more desirable than an escape from sanity, a flight into unreason, is to utilize the best reason within our capabilities. Our predicaments are due to faulty thinking and blind uncontrolled emotionality. We need more thoughtfulness, not less. The society that does not value the trained intelligence is doomed. We need a fusion of our intellectual potential with the best possible training of our emotions.

The hippie "love" scene is interesting, but only the naïve will take it at its face value. For some hippies, it is a thin veneer that barely covers strong feelings of anger. For others, it is an excuse to be promiscuous. Aggressiveness, especially during youth, is a drive which exists in almost every species. To deny it is not the healthiest way to deal with it. It would seem preferable to guide it into constructive channels.

Nor is there some innate goodness in yearning to return to nature. This perennial human dream is a fraud. How far back shall we go? To the Neanderthal man, disease-ridden, destructive, and murderous? Perhaps to the Europe of the eleventh century with its 70 years of famine, its wars unequaled in savagery, its black plagues? That primitive man lived a harmonious serene life is a palpable falsehood. If we are ever to achieve common human love and brotherhood, it will be by going forward, not backward. Man's brain is evolving in the direction of an increasing complexity—toward greater associational capacities and more intricate servomechanisms. The evolutionary direction seems to be toward an enhanced use of reason and an increased scrutiny of our universe and of ourselves. Nor can we expect that this surging pattern of evolving man will stand still, much less recede. Each generation must defend the advances that have accrued and extend the growing edge of freedom, knowledge, and humanity.

Then those of faint heart tell us that tomorrow we may all be wiped out by the Bomb. Their wail, of course, has been the wail of the self-pitying over the juggernaut, the crossbow, the Gatling gun, poison gas, dynamite, the airplane, and many other devices of destruction. Meanwhile, people continue to live and survive at the base of Vesuvius, in the Kalahari Desert, and on the Los Angeles Freeway.

3 *"A chemical Nirvana is the same as a transcendental state*
which one has sweated and endured in order to achieve."

This is an important point. Does chemical self-transcendence
have the same impact as self-transcendence that comes after long
vigils, suffering, etc.? Is the reward for which one does not work
the same as the reward for which one does? The behavioral
scientists tell us that it is not. This is not a matter of Protestant
ethic or Judeo-Christian ideology. It goes far beyond those. It
is also the Buddhist ethic, and it spreads beyond the family of
man. Every mammalian species learns as a result of stimulation
of either the reward or punishment centers in the brain. If there
is no task—if the reward is without cost—what is learned? Evidence is accumulating that the psychedelics act at least in part on
the reward centers of the brain. It would seem that the price one
pays is an intrinsic part of the total transaction. Maslow has
said, "An unearned Paradise is worthless." I would add, "An
unearned Paradise can be harmful."

The end, of course, is not satori or any other ineffable state; rather,
such a state is the beginning. Mrs. Suzuki and others have written
that satori is not the goal, just the first step toward the goal. If
these states have any value, it must be reflected in better conduct
and greater awareness in this existence.

4 *"The goals of the older generation are too superficial*
and narrow. The computerized future will rob
man of his freedom and individuality."

It is true that the aspirations of the older generation are too material and shortsighted. It is not too well understood why this is
so. The life experience of each generation leaves an imprint upon
its members. Those who went through the Great Depression of

the 1930s remember that able-bodied men willing to do any kind of work might starve to death. They could watch their families starve. This experience left its mark. It led to an overdetermined concern with the material—with security. This misguided preoccupation with money and things must be corrected, not overcorrected.

The world of the future can be the most wonderful or the most horrible of worlds. If we drop out, stop using that superlative instrument man's forebrain, surrender the decision making to the demagogue, the inept, or the fool, we are lost. Then the great superstructure collapses, the knowledge of the centuries is burned or rots away. The fragile pyramid of men, standing on the spiritual shoulders of those who have gone before, shatters. It need not be so.

More viable, less illusory alternatives to chemical transcendence exist for those seeking meaning in their life and their world. There is one thing complicating these alternatives: They are difficult. They require patience and resolve. Such approaches as the training of the senses and the emotions, small encounter groups, and meditation—all these and many others are well worth exploring. Such subjects could revitalize a school's curriculum.

We are all concerned about the dehumanization of man by the machine. We wonder whether man will lose his individuality and wonderful spirit of inquiry to the computer. We worry whether the minds of our children will ever be controlled by some megapower structure. But the "Brave New World," if it ever comes, will not be imposed upon us by some mechanical or human dictator. No, Nirvana seekers will come begging for their portion of Soma. Chemical thought control will be spread, like the Childrens' Crusade, by pied pipers who promise a bliss that exceeds description.

MORNING GLORY SEEDS

The Indians of Mexico and Central America have long been aware of the mild hallucinatory effects of the wild tropical American morning glory. They call it *ololiuqui,* "the green serpent." It is used to achieve a dreamy state and has never been considered a religious aid like the peyote cactus and the psilocybin mushroom.

The popularity of certain varieties of morning glory seeds has waned since LSD has become so readily available to those who wish to trip out. When Albert Hofmann extracted six alkaloids from the morning glories *Ipomoea violacea* and *Rivea corymbosa,* two of them were found to be D-lysergic acid hydroxyethylamide and D-lysergic acid amide. These were weak hallucinogens related to LSD with a mild sedative property; but if enough of the dark brown seeds were ground and swallowed, an LSD-like effect was occasionally achieved.

The morning-glory-seed partaker has certain advantages and disadvantages to consider. Packets of the active variety can often be obtained in the local feed and seed store. The legal status of its use is unclear in many communities. On the other hand, the seeds have sometimes been treated with insecticides and fungicides, which may render them more toxic unless they are thoroughly cleansed. Even after such preparation the prolonged use of these seeds may be hazardous. The physiological properties of Hofmann's other four alkaloids have been incompletely studied. The suspicion exists that they have long-lasting effects on the smaller blood vessels of the body. Another thing that has not yet been explained is the variability in potency even in the same variety. The age of the seeds, the place where they were grown, and many other factors seem to vary the alkaloidal content. An emetic factor is also present causing nausea and occasional vomiting. Complications similar to those occurring with LSD have been mentioned in connection with morning-glory-seed ingestion. One suicide has been reported, as well as prolonged psychoses.

DIMETHYLTRYPTAMINE (DMT)

In nature DMT has been found in cohaba snuff, which among the Mura Indians is blown up the nose through a bird's hollow bone. DMT has been tried by many LSD users, but rarely does it displace LSD in their affections. It is known to be a "blast," suddenly inducing an awayness which is of brief duration. To some people this is frightening and unpleasant, but those who want to get way out relish it. If LSD becomes scarce, DMT may become more widespread, for it can be produced from precursors which are at hand.

When DMT is taken by mouth, only a stomachache may result. Therefore it is either injected into the muscles or smoked mixed with tobacco or marihuana. Intravenous DMT has an instantaneous and a much too overwhelming effect to be tried except by those who prefer to have the odds against them. It is also effective in the form of an enema. Smoking DMT is slightly less dramatic. Some LSDers who relish the contemplative effects of acid find DMT too overpowering, too distorting, and too uncontrollable. The long-term toxicity of this compound has not been thoroughly investigated. Diethyltryptamine and other tryptamines are known to induce similar hallucinogenic states. Most compounds of this series have not yet been studied outside of biochemistry laboratories.

PEYOTE AND MESCALINE

One of the ancient psychedelics is the peyote cactus (*Lophophora williamsii*). The dried buttons are still occasionally used today, although it is not easy to understand why this bitter, nauseating potion has any consumers when more refined and palatable products are available.

Peyote is the only legally sanctioned hallucinogen in the United States. The Indians of the Native American Church of North America are permitted its use, though only within the context of their formal religious ceremonies. Otherwise, it is an unlawful item for both Indians and non-Indians alike. The Neo-American church and one or two other non-Indian sects are attempting to obtain permission to use the cactus as a sacrament in their ceremonies.

Mescaline is the chief alkaloid extracted from peyote. Now it is produced synthetically. It is four thousand times weaker than LSD, but when enough is taken, the effects are approximately similar. When it was purified at the turn of the century, a few people, including Havelock Ellis and Weir Mitchell, were very impressed by the visual and mental changes it induced. But it never caught on. Perhaps the relative stability of the culture at that time prevented its widespread acceptance.

STP

After a pump-priming operation when free STP was distributed at "love-ins" on the West Coast, this drug joined the list of psychedelics. It had previously been tested on laboratory animals only, not on man. This is further evidence of the slight value that some people place on their mental health. STP is about one-fiftieth as potent as LSD; when taken in large quantities, it can induce prolonged and intense reactions resembling reactions to the other psychedelics.

A suspicion exists that more than one compound is being peddled under the name "STP." Since this name is a takeoff on a motoroil additive, any concoction may be so labeled. Reports indicate that a few of the adverse effects resemble atropine intoxication, which is not to be anticipated from the pure STP. If chlorpromazine is given to STP trippers, a serious potentiation of effects is possible. For that reason bum trips that occur on STP should be managed by reassurance and support. If a chemical antidote is required, a barbiturate might be administered.

THE PSYCHEDELICS . . .
MARIHUANA

CHAPTER FOUR

THE GEOPOLITICS OF CANNABIS

From the Central Asian plateau comes the intoxicant second only to alcohol in global usage. It is the Indian hemp (*Cannabis sativa*), now cultivated and growing wild in many countries of the temperate and tropical zones.

The resin from the flowering tops of the female plant, whether smoked or eaten, is called *hashish* or *charas*. The male plant has less activity than the female, but the folktale that it is inert is incorrect. *Ganja* is less potent, being a mixture of resin, tops, and leaves. A third and still less potent product used in India is *bhang*, which is a tea made from the dried leaves and shoots. In strength, bhang is the equivalent of the American marihuana, having perhaps only a sixth of that of hashish. Hemp seeds themselves have negligible activity and are sold as birdseed in this country. They have been sterilized so that plants cannot be grown from them. Rope and textiles are made from the stalks.

Over the centuries its consumption spread from China to India, the Middle East, and Africa. From there it extended to South America, Central America, and in the past 50 years, to North America and Europe. It is a drug of many local names, the more common being "weed," "pot," "grass," and "tea." A "lid" consists of about an ounce of the green leaves, from which the stems and dirt must be cleaned before they are rolled into cigarette papers. The crudely rolled cigarettes are "joints," "reefers," or "sticks." The smoke has an acrid, aromatic odor not unlike burning alfalfa. It may persist for hours in a closed space. Incense is sometimes burned to mask the characteristic odor. The butts are called "roaches" and are retrieved for future use with a variety of "roach holders." The folklore states that the roaches are more potent than the joint itself.

The American variety (*Cannabis americana*) is grown in vacant lots, in flower boxes, or on railroad and highway rights-of-way. It is of poor quality. Better marihuana is grown in Mexico and other warm and humid countries. It is smuggled across the border by individuals or in medium-sized loads in trucks, boats, and planes. Occasionally a border-town salesman will collect twice for his marihuana, once when he makes the sale and later when he informs the American Customs. Only a small amount of the stronger hashish is seen on the American market. The channel from grower to smuggler to "pusher" to consumer still remains outside the organized narcotics ring, but violence and hijacking are known. Trading in marihuana is a profitable venture which attracts a variety of people, from criminal types to students who have purchased a kilo and want to retain a part and sell the rest for the original cost.

After World War I, marihuana was introduced into the United States by jazz musicians and later spread to minority groups, particularly those in slums. Artists and the "beat" and "hip" sets became involved. Then youngsters on high school and college campuses took up the habit. In recent years it has partially infiltrated the whiskey-drinking middle class. In India the use of Cannabis is looked upon as old-fashioned by the younger set. In the United States, however, it is definitely "in" at present. It is worth noting that India and Morocco have their hashish Skid Rows just as we have our Skid Rows based on alcohol.

It is interesting that every civilized country including the countries of its origin has regulations forbidding the sale of Cannabis. The most extreme seems to be a recent Nigerian regulation making its production or sale punishable by death. That law was passed after a series of destructive riots attributed to marihuana-induced violence. Egypt also has a death penalty on the law books, but it is not known whether it has ever been meted out. In 1961 the United States signed a United Nations treaty penalizing the growth, transportation, and sale of Cannabis. Our laws derive from the Marihuana Tax Act of 1937 and are enforced by narcotics agents. On the state level, marihuana is generally included in uniform narcotics laws which make traffic, possession, and use felonious. The penalties for usage and possession are severe, particularly since marihuana is a rather mild hallucinogen and not a narcotic. We are witnessing a considerable controversy at this time regarding its safety and legal status. An attempt will be made here to present and clarify these issues.

The realistic dangers of being apprehended for usage or possession are forceful and cogent reasons for desisting. This can hardly be put in clearer language than that used by the founder of the marihuana cult in this country. The jazz musician Mezz Mezzrow, who eventually stopped smoking pot, said, "I laid off five years ago, and if anybody asks my advice today, I tell them straight to steer clear of it because it carries a rap. That's my final word to all the cats—today I know of one very bad thing the tea can do to you—it can put you in jail. 'Nuff said."

CHEMISTRY

Chemically, a large number of related compounds are found in marihuana. A cannabinol has recently been synthesized which is stable and best duplicates most of the effects of the drug. The tetrahydrocannabinols are unstable compounds, and it is for that reason that research reports have been conflicting. The amount of the active substance in each batch varies, depending on the soil, moisture, time of harvesting, storage, and other factors. Smoking is regarded as the most active way the drug can be used. Eating hashish tends to reduce its activity, but potent preparations are effective orally.

PHYSICAL AND PSYCHOLOGICAL EFFECTS

Physiologically, dilation of the pupils frequently occurs, but it is not as pronounced as with LSD or the amphetamines. Presumably, increased secretion of adrenalin produces a rise and then a sudden fall in blood sugar, which calls forth an increased appetite, especially for sweets. Hunger is observed more often in the beginner than in the chronic user. In contrast, other psychedelics diminish interest in food. Another difference is the drowsiness that many mention toward the end of a marihuana session, whereas wakefulness is the rule with the strong psychedelics. The experienced user has little difficulty in appearing and acting normally. It is when he is under stress that difficulties in judgment and coordination may arise. A blood test to detect tetrahydrocannabinol is about to become available.

The physical side effects are not of great significance except in heavy users. Inflammation of the whites of the eyes, the throat, and bronchial tubes are occasionally noted. In heavy smokers,

emphysema and chronic bronchitis may eventually develop because of the need for prolonged, deep, and retained inhalation,
which is a part of the smoker's technique for obtaining a maximal
effect. Not knowing the technique and what to look for, some
novices say that marihuana is "a nothing." Neither tolerance
nor withdrawal effects are noted after daily use. Psychic dependence is certainly known. As one young person said when
asked about frequency of usage, "Pot? It is my life."

The psychological changes mimic those of a tiny dose of a drug
like LSD. Loosening of emotional and social restraints, a feeling
of relaxation or euphoria, distortions of time and space, illusions,
a fantasy type of thinking—all can be experienced. At times,
mental confusion, rather terrifying paranoid thoughts, and anxiety
pervade. As just indicated, the effects of marihuana depend upon
whether the smoker is a novice or experienced. The new user is
more apt to have either no symptoms or an overwhelming loss of
control. Protracted laughter or tears are noted in the neophyte.
The old hand at marihuana is more likely to be quiet and intro-
spective.

More and more, marihuana is becoming a basic drug to which
other agents are added. Some smokers will spike their marihuana
with LSD or DMT. Heroin or cocaine is sometimes used in or
with the reefer. For many marihuana is a satisfactory relaxant,
and they do not escalate, but a few people demand stronger stuff
after a period of time on the weed.

Marihuana and LSD are used simultaneously for their additive
potential. Marihuana is commonly smoked while waiting for
LSD to take effect, to intensify the "high," or to prolong the
psychedelic state. *Potentiation*, as this pharmacological action
is called, may be either successful or excessively successful so that
an overwhelming condition is produced. Not infrequently users
of both "acid" and "pot" will mention that the latter will produce effects as strong as their LSD experiences.

Since marihuana has both a stimulating and a depressing effect, an occasional LSD user in a prolonged anxiety reaction will try to quiet himself with a joint. This may only aggravate the tension state. More than one person has reported to me that after a shattering time with LSD, his subsequent trials of marihuana were also unpleasant.

As the smoker learns to "maintain," that is, to reach a level and hold it, he becomes able to regulate the degree to which he will fantasize, depersonalize, or enjoy his altered perceptions. Thus he can withdraw into a dreamy reverie, get out of himself, look at art works, listen to music, or socialize. He finds those things that were difficult to do while sober are made easier by marihuana. This is the seductive aspect of the drug for young people, particularly those who are dependent, unsure of themselves, or unhappy. The shy, inadequate, or chronically perturbed find the marihuana way of life far easier than their ordinary existence. It provides them with a solution to their conflicts about aggression, sexuality, and maturation. The painful process of problem solving is bypassed. Unfortunately, it is this same process which is an intrinsic part of growing up. The marihuana solution becomes a substitute for the learning encounters which are the result of meeting difficulties and enduring or solving them.

Most studies of student pot smoking indicate that a major reason for starting the practice is to conform to one's group of acquaintances. Curiosity about the effects is certainly a contributing element. The statements of friends that it is a high make it attractive. These and the desire to be "in" readily persuade the neophyte. Even negative or negligible reactions to the first few reefers do not deter most initiates. The social closeness of small-group communal sharing of the cigarette and the drug-provided excuse to speak out or act out have certain attractions. If boredom and loneliness can be set aside, if pleasure otherwise not quite obtainable can be felt, why not? Preexisting discontent, restless, depressed moods, and chronic feelings of tension are predisposing emotional factors. The use of marihuana is clearly increasing.

The "pothead," whose life revolves around marihuana, must be clearly distinguished from the occasional user, who may go for long periods without indulging. The young pothead smokes whenever he can, and particularly when the world seems difficult and overwhelming. An argument with his parents, a breakup with the girlfriend, a failing grade at school—these and other minor and major frustrations are dissolved in the smoke from a joint. No effort is expended, yet the problem disappears as long as one is "stoned." The projection of one's own inadequacies is a frequent mechanism for dealing with them. It is much less crushing to live in a miserable world than to be a miserable person.

MARIHUANA AND ALCOHOL

The comparison of marihuana and alcohol is instructive because of the many similarities and the occasional dissimilarity. Both are releasing, or disinhibiting, drugs. Acting-out behavior which is ordinarily controlled may become overt. Asocial and antisocial acts are possible, but these seem to be unleashings of underlying personality patterns rather than drug-specific activities. Thus sexual activities may occur which would not transpire under normal conditions. Neither drug is an aphrodisiac; both merely dissolve moral resistance. The time distortion which marihuana induces may magnify the sensual aspects. The passivity that is claimed for marihuana and the aggressiveness that is claimed for alcohol are overgeneralizations. In fact, any sort of behavior is possible with both drugs.

Like alcohol, marihuana may produce violent reactions in a few unsophisticated individuals. As with alcohol, discriminate, moderate use may have no adverse effects. Similarly, the heavy consumers of both intoxicants, especially vulnerable individuals, can experience temporary psychotic reactions. An organic dementia following excessive use of both agents has been described. Naturally, the unstable and immature are prone to misuse these superego-dissolving drugs. They then become neglectful, slovenly, irresponsible, and unmotivated and proceed to lose out or "drop out."

The differences between alcohol and marihuana, aside from their legal status, are worth noting. The infrequent user of either drug is not likely to get into trouble with it. Liver damage does not occur with marihuana abuse as it can in the severe alcoholic. Whether one is less aggressive under the influence of marihuana is doubtful. Personality traits and the social setting are more likely to determine whether impulsive and hostile acts will occur. Because of the sensory distortions of marihuana, more paranoid ideas are entertained or acted upon.

Two safety factors are present with marihuana smoking that are not present with most hallucinogens. One is its rather mild action. The other is that a desired immediate level can be reached while inhaling; since the active ingredients go directly into the brain from the bloodstream, overdosing oneself is less possible than it is in swallowing a capsule of LSD. This control is analogous to the social drinker who knows that two Martinis is right for him—and stops. Both can be mistaken on occasion.

MARIHUANA FACTS AND FABLES

The controversies surrounding marihuana concern a number of misunderstandings and extremist opinions. These can be enumerated:

1 *Marihuana is a narcotic*

Logically, marihuana should be removed from the state narcotics laws and placed in the category of dangerous drugs. At present, the penalties in cases involving marihuana exceed those for LSD, a much more potent and hazardous drug. This anomalous situation ought to be remedied—not as a response to pressure groups, but because it is a rational step.

2 Marihuana is less harmful than alcohol

We tend to compare unequal quantities of these agents. A puff on a joint of weak, locally grown marihuana is no more or less harmful than a drink of whiskey. But a single drag on a strong reefer may stone the user as would a half-pint of hard liquor. Both intoxications have their dangers in motor incoordination and impaired judgment. Chronic, prolonged alcoholism is a serious problem; chronic, prolonged usage of marihuana can have serious consequences. Reports of marihuana psychoses and dementia have come from every country where marihuana has been used for long periods of time. The American experience is insufficient to confirm or deny the long-term complications of this drug. The physical complications of severe alcoholism exceed those of severe marihuana usage. Alcohol is a legally acceptable way to escape; marihuana carries the realistic danger of jail. This very real danger must be included in the calculations of those who are faced with a decision to experiment or not to experiment.

3 If alcohol is legal, why not marihuana

The logic of legalizing one potentially dangerous item because we have another, culturally accepted potion which has a potential for danger is questionable. It would be more proper to try to eliminate the proved hazards of excessive alcoholism than add another substance whose long-term effects have not been carefully explored. In India and the Middle East, where hashish is used, many writers have warned against its damaging effects. The Egyptian literature notes that over a quarter of Egyptian admissions to mental hospitals for psychotic states are hashish psychoses.

4 *Marihuana is a religious drug*

It is true that the Yogis used Indian hemp as an aid to meditation, but it was also used by the Hashishins to work up
the courage to assassinate, and by the Thugs as a reward for
strangling their victims. This point illustrates how a disinhibiting agent of any sort can induce the most laudable or
the most despicable behavior. It all depends on the context
in which it is taken. Thus there are no good drugs or bad
drugs, no religious or sacrilegious drugs. It all depends on
the purpose to which the drug is put.

5 *Keeping marihuana illegal merely increases
its use by those who want to defy authority*

This is partly true; the rebellious juvenile will obtain an added
charge out of an illegal act. On the other hand, the fact that
marihuana usage carries a penalty deters others. Legalizing
marihuana would unquestionably increase its consumption.
But legalization would not give blanket permission for all to
use the drug. At most, it would come under provisions similar to those for alcohol, making its use for minors illegal.
Driving or disorderly conduct while under its influence would
still be punishable. In other words, the majority of those
who now use pot would still be using it illegally if the present
laws were abolished.

6 *We each have the freedom to take whatever drugs
we wish so long as no one else is harmed*

It is getting more and more difficult in our complex, inter-
locking, urban society to do something which does not reverberate to those we are responsible for, those we love, and
those in close touch with us. Do we have the freedom to use
marihuana? If so, where is the cutoff point? Should the
"junkie" have the freedom to use heroin? What is striking
in the arguments of those who demand their individual free-

dom is their unawareness of their group responsibilities. An intimate reciprocal relationship between our freedoms and our responsibilities exists.

7 *If marihuana is not addictive, why not legalize it*

Physical dependence is only one kind of undesirable effect from a drug. Cocaine is not physically addictive. The issue is not one of addiction versus nonaddiction, but of harmfulness versus nonharmfulness. In considering the apparent harmlessness of marihuana, it must be recalled that the American variety has a low resin content. If marihuana is legalized and the stronger hashish becomes popular, it will produce an increased number of adverse reactions, perhaps equaling or exceeding those with alcohol. Hashish is becoming available in this country in increasing quantities.

8 *Marihuana use leads to heroin*

This is apparently untrue. What does seem to happen is that whenever asocial drug taking starts, additional drugs are likely to be tried. The histories obtained from people in deep trouble with drugs often tell of marihuana, airplane cement, or cough syrup being used first. Then there is progression to LSD, DMT, or mescaline. The pathway to amphetamines and sleepers is direct or via the hallucinogens. Very few go on to heroin, but some do. Would they have "turned on" to heroin anyway? It will be interesting to see what happens to the hemp user of today. In 20 years will he still be content with pot? Except for alcoholics, marihuana's role seems to be that of a basal drug for all "heads"—"acid," "hop," and "pill."

9 *Marihuana legalization would lead to legalization of drugs like LSD*

This sort of argument is not valid, and the question must be resolved on other grounds.

10 We should prosecute the user and make an example of him in order to control abuse

This is no way to solve a growing problem. Controls seem to be necessary, but they should be applied at the smuggler-pusher level rather than the user level. The laws against marihuana possession and usage are much too stringent and may be doing more harm than good. Over 5,000 first-time arrests a year for possession or usage are made in California alone; most of these involve juveniles.

11 This is the age of drugs, so why not pot

The proposition that this is the age of drugs may be quite incorrect. A study of drug-taking habits indicates great interest in innumerable vegetables, volatile gases, and a wide variety of mind-altering herbs and other panaceas through the ages. But even if it were true that we are consuming more drugs for more reasons, the question should be, "What is the proper place and use of all these drugs in our society?" rather than a question that provides an excuse to take all drugs.

12 Pot helps me understand myself and the world around me

This may be about as true as "In vino veritas."

13 Marihuana is immoral

No drug is moral or immoral. Rather, it is the manner of usage that determines its rightness or wrongness.

14 Marihuana makes me more creative

Correction: It makes you feel more creative. Actually, your drive to create may be considerably reduced, and drive is as important as any factor in the creative process.

15 *God made marihuana; therefore we have a right to use it*

God also made poison ivy, cholera, and leprosy. That something exists in nature does not have any bearing on its merits.

16 *Research will give us the answers*
    about the dangers of marihuana

The danger that all are concerned about is its long-term effect. Investigators will have to observe subjects for two or three decades before that question can be answered. Those calling for research to determine our position about marihuana have unrealistic expectations about the rapidity of a reliable response.

WITCHES' BREWS
& THE LIKE

CHAPTER FIVE

We have made real progress since the Middle Ages. During that dark interval in man's struggle for light, draughts of strange potions made the imbiber believe that she could fly through the air on a broomstick. Nowadays, with the psychedelics, the broomstick has become quite unnecessary. What do we know of some of the ancient herbs which bewitched the witches?

Some minor misuse of them is encountered even today. These brews all belong to the Solanaceae family. Belladonna, or deadly nightshade (*Atropa belladonna*), has a varied history. Professional poisoners depended upon it even before the time of the Borgias. Beautiful women made themselves more beautiful by dilating their pupils with a drop of the extract in each eye. Belladonna was probably put into the wine during bacchanalias to increase the inebriated revelry and the unrestrained excitement.

Atropine, the alkaloid in belladonna, now has prosaic uses in the treatment of peptic ulcers and the dilation of the pupil prior to eye examinations. An occasional instance of delirium is reported from its consumption in larger than the recommended amounts.

Datura stramonium has many common names. It is called Jamestown or Jimson weed (from Jamestown, Virginia), stinkweed, thorn apple, and devil's-apple. It contains atropine and hyoscyamine and was well known to the sorcerers and witches of yore. This was one of the major ingredients of the libation mixed for the witches' Sabbath, when all sorts of hallucinated and actual goings-on took place. Jimson weed used by mistake as a green in a salad produced a 10-day madness in a platoon of redcoats who had been called to Jamestown to put down Nathaniel Bacon's rebellion against the British. The American Indians knew Jimson weed well, and some of them employed it as an ordeal in rites held to initiate their young men into manhood. The Colombian Indians used to give *Datura* to the slaves of dead masters and wives of dead husbands to put them into a drunken stupor before burying them alive with the deceased.

This common poisonous weed still reverberates in the modern world. A few schoolboys in Ventura County, California have been found intoxicated and sick after chewing the leaves. Their dilated pupils, flushed faces, dry mouths, galloping pulses, and florid delirium reproduced a 2,000-year-old pattern. Asthmador is an old-fashioned asthma remedy that contains belladonna and stramonium, among other ingredients. It can be purchased over the counter in a few drugstores that still stock it. Recently, some young folks discovered that one can go out of one's mind by taking large amounts of Asthmador. Just why this outmoded preparation is still on sale without controls is obscure. Occasionally, cases in a confused, hallucinatory state have been brought to emergency hospitals for treatment of Jimson weed poisoning.

Henbane also belongs in this family. It is a bane not only to hens but also to human beings. Its official name is *Hyoscyamus niger*, and it contains scopolamine. When administered in the old days, it cast a spell over the victim, who routinely reported seeing demons and scenes of Hell—the precursor of today's "bum trip." Nor was it necessary to swallow the henbane; an ointment containing it rubbed on the skin would induce a frenzied, nightmarish drunk. Scopolamine, its alkaloid, had a brief interval of use as a truth serum and, later, as a means of inducing twilight sleep in obstetric patients during childbirth. Henbane has not yet been discovered by our youth.

The mandrake-man relationship is one of those strange and ancient tales of gloom and doom. Mandrake (*Mandragora officinarum*) was used as a truth drug by the Chinese long before the Christian Era. After confession of a crime, the mandrake wine served to numb the pain of the prisoner's death by torture. It is mentioned in the Old Testament as a fertility potion; no doubt, the fact that the forked root had some slight resemblance to the human limbs was the basis for the belief that it was one. Roman soldiers gave it to those about to be crucified to numb the senses. Professional poisoners employed it during the Dark Ages. Its most common use was as an aphrodisiac. In quantities less than those which caused delirium and death, it was presumed to be a love philtre. Only qualified mandrake witchwives were able to collect the plant, for it was supposed to provoke unearthly shrieks while being pulled from the soil—shrieks so appalling that anyone hearing them went insane forthwith.

There are dozens of other deliriants, intoxicants, psychedelics, confusants, and turmoilizers. Some have yet to make a public appearance; some are used medicinally, but are not a part of today's drug dilemma. Alcohol, of course, requires a book of its own. Tobacco is not being discussed here because it is more a conditioned reflex than a mind-altering drug.

Two spices from the nutmeg tree (*Myristica fragrans*) have been taken to provide a crude delirium. On odd occasions a youngster or a prisoner will get drunk on nutmeg or mace, particularly the former. This peculiar practice is sufficiently well known in jails that these spices are kept under lock. One-half to one ounce of the powdered nutmeg (two to six nutmegs) provokes euphoria, illusions, hallucinations, and later, drowsiness and sleep. The onset of symptoms is delayed for hours, and some of the reactions can last for days. In the above amounts, there are many unpleasant side effects: cramps, headache, weak pulse, vertigo, pressure in the chest, and sometimes physical collapse. Extreme thirst is often mentioned, and the delirium frequently alternates with a stupor. One patient I saw expressed considerable apprehension, suspiciousness, and feelings of impending doom. A few reports of death in children who accidentally swallowed large amounts of pounded nutmeg are in the literature. A century ago the rumor that sufficient nutmeg could induce an abortion was rather widespread. In the large amounts taken it rarely produced the desired result but did result in poisoning.

"Blue velvet" enjoyed a degree of popularity as a sedative a few years ago, particularly in Great Britain. It was a mixture of paregoric, a camphorated tincture of opium, and Pyribenzamine, an antihistamine. The combination was strained and "mainlined," although neither substance was manufactured for use in this fashion. When any preparation is directly injected into a vein, it passes through the right side of the heart and then is pumped into the lungs. The fine capillaries of the lungs act as an ultrafilter, retaining those bits of material which have passed through the absorbent-cotton strainer. Those who shoot blue velvet, and indeed the mainliners of any substance, are liable to come down with many small lung solidifications called *granulomas*. These are tiny nodules caused by the captured substance, which may be talcum or dirt, and the lung's subsequent inflammatory reaction to it. When enough of these accumulate, shortness of breath results.

A while ago an upsurge of dried-banana-peel smoking was the rage in Haight-Ashbury and other "hippie" outposts. This fad has died down despite the fact that the scrapings of the inner pulp of the commercial banana (*Musa sapientum*) are quite harmless and are also quite ineffective. In one study of this pseudo-psychedelic, no mental effects and only some mild and brief physical effects were noted. It could not be distinguished by experienced marihuana smokers from orange pekoe tea rolled into cigarettes. Those who obtained a "kick" from "mellow yellow" demonstrated once again the power of human suggestibility. Every few weeks a new rumor comes out of the hippie undergroup: use baby wood rose seeds, smoke spider webs, eat old wheat germ, try rotten green peppers, chew Scotch broom, or put an aspirin in a cigarette. Certainly, there are plenty of odds and ends that can intoxicate, but the old witches' brews were probably as potent and as dangerous as many of our twentieth-century concoctions.

THE OPIATES

CHAPTER SIX

THE LESSONS OF HISTORY

Only those facets of the intriguing history of *opium* will be mentioned that shed light upon our current drug dilemma. Opium was in use for thousands of years before its addictive properties were established. The Asian peasant smoking his pipe was quietly tied to the habit, though smoking was an inefficient way to extract euphoria from opium. The supply was plentiful, and his way of life did not require alertness or complex thinking. His dreamy state hardly harmed anyone, and it was a refuge from the raw misery of the day. When gum opium and laudanum (tincture of opium) came into use in the bustling cities of the world, it soon became evident that the dependence was detrimental to the urban user, his family, and his society. In England in the late eighteenth and early nineteenth century, opium "eating" was a middle- and upper-class phenomenon, just as the psychedelics are today. In fact, some of the parallels between the two situations are fascinating. As the magnitude of the problem was recognized, it was blamed on the difficult, unsettled times. Many artists, poets, and writers of the day were involved. De Quincey was most closely identified with opium because of his *Confessions of an English Opium Eater*. Poe, Coleridge, Swinburne, and Elizabeth Barrett Browning thought it a panacea for man's ills at first but later inveighed against it.

It should not be imagined that these gifted people derived their creative productions from opium. On the contrary, Samuel Coleridge blamed his later inability to produce, as well as his barbarous neglect of his family, on opium eating. During the early years of his habit, while he was still a student at Cambridge, he was enthused enough to write to his brother, "Laudanum gives me repose, not sleep, but you know how divine that repose is, what a spot of enchantment, a green spot of fountains and flowers and trees in the very heart of a wasteland of sands." But as the author of *Kubla Khan* learned more about the drug, his opinion changed. He called it "an accursed habit, a wretched vice, a species of madness, a derangement, an utter impotence of the volition." Finally, Coleridge was able to overcome his addiction and became a strong advocate of its control. About the situation in early nineteenth-century England, he wrote, "The practise of taking opium is dreadfully spread. Throughout Lancashire and Yorkshire it is the common dram of the lower orders of people. In the small town of Thorpe, the druggist informed me that he commonly sold on market days two or three pounds of opium and a gallon of laudanum—all among the laboring classes. Surely, this demands legislative interference."

The story, a century ago, in the United States was not too dissimilar. Many patent medicines were laced with opium. Opium was in the bottle but not on the label. Even baby's soothing syrups contained a tot's share. Infants became very irritable when deprived of their customary soothing syrup.

Another source of the habit was those Chinese who arrived with their opium pipes to work on the transcontinental railroad and in the gold-mining camps. The custom of smoking opium spread from the dens of Chinatown to the sporting blood, the prostitute, and even to the youths of the respectable middle class.

After the purified alkaloid *morphine* was synthesized, and after the hypodermic syringe was invented in the 1850s, the quality of addictiveness intensified manifold. During the Civil War, thousands of the wounded, the malarial, and the dysenteric were seeking relief. Some doctors believed that giving morphine under the skin would avoid morphinism. In fact, the contrary was true. Large amounts were dispensed with the new syringes. Dependence on morphine injections came to be known as "the soldier's disease."

The easy access to gum opium, the patent medicines which no one had under supervision or control, and the incautious use of morphine by syringe caused enormous numbers to become addicted. It is estimated that 1¼ million (4 percent of our population) were caught up in some form of the opiate habit 100 years ago. Naturally, new patent medicines were developed as cures for the opium habit and morphine craving. They were successful because opium was one of their ingredients.

The tragic story was not yet ended. In 1898 morphine was acetylated, and early trials indicated that the product cured both opium and morphine addiction. It was received with such enthusiasm and high hopes that it was named from "hero"—*heroin*.

Today, about one person in two thousand (0.05 percent of the population) is an opiate addict in this country. Nevertheless, the condition of the addict has deteriorated because of the illegal status of opiates and the profits that are being made out of the narcotic traffic. If the organized crime ring could be eliminated, practically all problems with narcotic addiction would disappear. These people are known; it is scandalous that they are permitted to continue to exploit the most miserable person of all—the addict. The things that a heroin user must and will do in order to maintain his habit are so degrading that it is hardly defensible to speak of the freedom to use such a drug, although a few people do. Those who still speak of the benefits of the English system have not yet heard that the English are currently modifying their policies. The English system has provided medical treatment of addicts and supplied their needs by prescriptions. Unfortunately, the buildup of tolerance and the resale of heroin by the registered addict to his friends or for profit have caused sufficient abuses of this benign and humane effort that heroin addicts are increasing by 50 percent yearly in England. The number is still not great, but the increase in young, middle-class addicts is causing real concern.

Three lessons can be derived from the foregoing. One is that it may take a long time before some of the adverse effects of a drug become apparent. The connection between alcohol excesses and cirrhosis of the liver or neuritis was not understood for thousands of years. The addictive potential of the opiates was not recognized for centuries. Another lesson is that altering the cultural setting or the mode of taking the drug may cause new problems to become manifest. The very powerful derivatives morphine and heroin and the use of the hypodermic needle created a quicker and stronger dependence. The third lesson is that when the middle- or upper-class intellectuals introduce a drug fad, they are just as likely to choose poorly as when it seeps up from the slums. The fact that the intelligentsia introduces a drug fad does not guarantee its wisdom or its safety.

CLASSIFICATIONS

The opiates are derivatives from the resin of the pod of the opium poppy (*Papaver somniferum*). The commonly encountered alkaloids include morphine and codeine; heroin is produced from morphine by treating it with acetic acid. A number of synthetic drugs are also used as analgesics but have an addictive potential, Demerol, Dilaudid, and methadone being the best known of these. The major item (and the most addictive) in illicit commerce is heroin. It is ordinarily purchased in cellophane "decks." This is a highly "cut" heroin, so weak at times that it cannot maintain a habit or "hook" the user. Heroin comes across the national boundary by every conceivable mode of transportation. It usually arrives as 80 percent heroin, but it is cut with milk sugar, quinine, or baking soda as it passes down the hierarchy of big- to small-time "pushers." It reaches the ultimate consumer with a 0 to 5 percent heroin content. These days, 5 percent heroin is considered good stuff. An analysis of various samples obtained from pushers revealed that anything from 0 to 77 percent heroin might be obtained. It is evident that the addict runs a risk of poisoning himself if he happens to obtain uncut or insufficiently cut heroin. Heroin has no use in medicine in this country, and the entire supply of the drug passes through a complicated and sordid black-market mazeway.

Morphine is a standard pain reliever still widely used, but eventually it will be replaced by an equally effective analgesic which is not addictive. The morphine habit is much less frequently seen than it used to be; very occasionally a doctor or nurse becomes addicted. Morphine comes from licit sources (faked doctor's prescriptions, drug-store robberies) and does not often fall into the hands of pushers.

Codeine is an effective analgesic with a much lower addiction potential than either heroin or morphine. When heroin addicts are separated from their supply, they may resort to codeine to tide them over. Both morphine and heroin addicts attempting to avoid withdrawal symptoms often resort to codeine cough syrups, which in a number of states are exempt narcotics, that is, can be purchased without a prescription. Elixir of Terpin Hydrate with

Codeine, Cheracol, Cosanyl, and Romilar are some of the preparations containing codeine or codeine-like compounds.

Demerol is a widely used pain reliever which is less addictive than morphine. Addicts have been made by the careless use of Demerol by physicians. If an illness is terminal, there is no reason to withhold potent analgesics of this sort; however, chronic pain in a person who will live for many years must be treated with the greatest skill to provide relief and yet avoid addiction. Demerol is sometimes available from pushers. Dilaudid and Pantopon are other potent pain allayers with definite addiction potential. At one time they were a problem, but now they are rarely seen in the world of the addict.

Methadone is a synthetic narcotic which is less euphoriant than heroin, but certainly must be considered an addictive drug. It is mentioned here because a recent treatment program substitutes methadone tablets for injectable heroin. Apparently, the addict can be kept comfortable with no need to increase the methadone. Heroin taken by someone on full doses of methadone will not produce the heroin "high." *Cyclazozine* is a recently developed synthetic drug which is also being used in the treatment of the addict. It seems to be nonaddictive and decreases the craving of the "hophead." It, too, can block the euphoriant effect of heroin.

THE YOUNG NARCOTIC ADDICT

Although the number of school-age narcotic addicts is not great (as compared to marihuana, LSD, or pep-pill users), their situation is deplorable, and every effort should be made to identify and treat these young people, as well as to prevent others from joining them. The things that an addict must do to maintain, say, a $50-a-day habit are so debasing that his plight must be considered worse than that of the user of any other type of drugs. Not only must addicts steal or "hustle" the money, but they also must deal with criminals and spend their waking hours obsessed with keeping supplied with enough "H" to keep them comfortable. Theirs is a pressure-cooker existence that ends nowhere.

Many contributory factors enter into the narcotic addiction of a young person. They can be enumerated:

1 Most young addicts are from minority groups in which households are so disrupted that the family unit hardly exists.

2 Peers and peer values often are critical factors in heroin usage. In some urban slum areas, boyfriends turn on girlfriends, gangs turn on newcomers, and older siblings may turn on younger ones. The male-female ratio is about 5 to 1.

3 Within a framework of chaotic familial and social life, dependent, passive, immature youngsters are more vulnerable and are spoken of as having an "addictive personality." That any personality type might get locked into a heroin habit is unquestionable. When a relatively mature person becomes addicted for some reason, the possibility of a cure is much more favorable.

4 Those who become addicts seem to have the greatest difficulty in handling anxiety, depression, and their adolescent drives. Delinquent behavior often existed prior to drug usage. Drug usage, of course, promotes further delinquent activities.

5 Prior nonnarcotic drug usages may have facilitated the introduction to heroin. The use of an illicit drug of any type permits easier movement to more potent drug groups. For some people a drug barrier seems to exist; once it is breached, all sorts of drugs might be used.

6 The active recruitment of new consumers by pushers is hardly necessary under present conditions. Persistent "hippie" rumors that some LSD is spiked with heroin to create more heroin addicts are as difficult to believe as the old tale of pushers turning on schoolchildren. Grade school children have become addicted, but not through pushers. As a rule, users obtain gratification from turning nonusers on. Their motives range from hostility to love.

PHYSICAL AND PSYCHOLOGICAL EFFECTS

The procurement of "kicks" from heroin is highly variable. The first few exposures, especially if the heroin is "mainlined" or "skin-popped," may provide an orgasm-like effect. Eventually, little is derived from an injection beyond a reduction in tension, a quieting, and relief from premonitory withdrawal sickness. Many established addicts are more concerned with avoiding the abstinence syndrome than with gaining some positive elevation of mood. There are a few addiction-prone individuals who "shoot smack" once or twice a week for long periods without becoming addicted. No doubt their resistance to addiction is due to the very dilute material now in circulation. If the 20 percent heroin of the "good old days" were available, we would have a new flood of youthful "dope fiends."

Sudden discontinuance of a substantial heroin intake leads to a profound autonomic storm. Every orifice pours forth its secretion or excretion. Muscles twitch or cramp, and convulsions can occur; gooseflesh and a constant feeling of being cold, chills and fever leave the person in withdrawal with a compulsion to secure relief by obtaining, somehow, the drug for which every cell in his body is shrieking. It is during the withdrawal period that the heroin addict will resort to violence to obtain relief. After two or three days the symptoms gradually abate, and the physical dependence on the presence of opiates in the body is eventually lost; the psychic dependence remains for a much longer period, perhaps for a lifetime.

There is some research evidence that physical (cellular) dependence may last even after the addict has recovered and feels well. In a subtle form some of the physiological reactions in the abstaining addict's body are altered for weeks, perhaps months.

Psychological dependence is the craving for the euphoria or the knowledge that narcotics equal relief from tensions and from being sick with withdrawal symptoms. Even addicts who have been "clean" for many years relate that this memory remains with them and that they must be careful during periods of despondency not to slip back.

COMPLICATIONS

If pure and germ-free heroin were available to the consumer, if his technique of injection ensured sterility, if the dose did not have to be pyramided, and if precise quality control were guaranteed, many of the diseases of heroin usage could be avoided. Actually, none of these criteria is met, for one reason or other. Therefore, we see a number of virulent sequelae to heroin usage. The length of life of the addict is significantly shorter than that of his non-addicted peer. In England, where pure heroin and disposable syringes are provided free by the National Health Service, it is of interest that the same percentages of the complications to be mentioned are reported as in the United States. This is a reflection of the basic personality of the addict, or what addiction does to the personality.

One group of these complications consists in infections from contaminated material or from the means of instilling the heroin into the vein or under the skin. Addicts have been known to die immediately after a self-administered intravenous injection, with only edema of the lungs found at autopsy. The virus of hepatitis is often transmitted when a number of people use the same syringe. Hepatitis is the most frequent complication of shooting heroin. It can be lethal or result in permanent liver damage. Pneumonia and tuberculosis are also common complications. Certain injected bacteria (*Streptococcus viridans*, for example) have a predilection to lodge on the heart valves and cause a serious condition called bacterial endocarditis. Heroin mainliners are much more apt to come down with endocarditis than nonusers. Other infectious diseases that have been reported from inadequately sterilized syringes are sepsis, syphilis, malaria, and tetanus. In recent years the majority of deaths from tetanus have been in the group of skin-popping addicts. Infections and abscesses of the skin are well known. Phlebitis is a painful swelling along the course of the inflamed vein, due to the instillation of irritating material. It has a series of secondary complications of its own, such as lung emboli.

Even aside from the above illnesses to which the addict is prone, his general nutrition and health are often poor. His food intake is haphazard, and money spent for food is considered wasted. His teeth lack ordinary attention, to say nothing of formal dental care. Skin infections due to dirt and scratching are not uncommon. These tend to heal poorly because of poor resistance. The female addict is an excellent candidate for all of the venereal diseases and considerable physical trauma.

The strength of the heroin being sold seems to grow weaker each year. As noted, some decks contain no heroin whatsoever. When a user happens to obtain reasonably potent material, he runs the risk of overdosing himself with it because tolerance to large quantities never has been acquired. Death from overdose ("O.D.") is all too well known. It has been estimated that 1 percent of all New York City addicts die each year from overdosage. Every heroin addict can expect to experience overdosage at least once. He may recover with or without treatment. Death is due to paralysis of the breathing center in the brain. Overdosage occurs in new users who take too much, in those who have lost their tolerance to heroin by being in jail or a hospital, and in those who obtain good heroin by mistake. When a pusher suspects that one of his customers may be an informer, he may deliberately give him uncut heroin, thereby permitting the "hype" to murder himself.

Another form of morbidity develops from the powder used to cut the heroin. Fine granules in the injected material cannot pass through the lungs, where they accumulate and form granulomas. They interfere with breathing, and eventually may occupy enough lung tissue to produce failure of respiration.

Death has occurred during the withdrawal period. Especially in older addicts with substantial habits, the heart may fail or the vascular system may collapse. "Cold turkey" is not for the elderly or frail; they should be gradually withdrawn to avoid sudden circulatory collapse.

DETECTION

The youthful abuser ordinarily starts with codeine or codeine-like cough syrups which also contain a fair amount of alcohol. These are usually sold in 4-oz. bottles and may be found in trash cans or vacant lots near the school or home. He may seem "away" or "high" to the observer. As interest in opiates increases, his school or work effectiveness diminishes. He may change his circle of friends, lose interest in his home life, sleep during the day, and go out at night.

If he graduates to heroin, his "outfit" may be found. This may be a regular hypodermic syringe or a contrivance with a needle and eyedropper which somehow accomplishes the purpose. At this point he requires sums of money which he can hardly come by from an allowance or job. He may steal from the family or strangers, pawn or sell household items, or become a small-time pusher himself. An addict may "turn a trick" to obtain money for a fix.

The most notable sign of active heroin taking is constricted pupils which do not dilate when a light is flashed on them. Sometimes these are called "pinpoint" pupils, and dark glasses may be worn to evade detection. The heroin user can pull himself together to

behave and respond rationally if challenged.   When the effects of
the drug have worn off, the pupil size becomes normal.

Needle-puncture marks or scars can be seen along the course of arm
and leg veins, and long-sleeved clothing is worn even in warm
weather to avoid showing the recent or old needle "tracks."   In
neighborhoods where addiction is quite common, these precautions
are not taken.

A doctor called upon to treat skin abscesses or hepatitis might sus-
pect prior skin popping or mainlining.   He should also be aware
of the bids experienced addicts make for narcotic drugs by per-
fectly simulating kidney colic or other painful conditions.   Both
the family and the doctor may be confronted with the runny nose,
muscle twitching, tearing, generalized aches, vomiting, diarrhea,
sweating, and other symptoms of narcotic withdrawal.   These are
not only evidence of addiction but also demonstrations of the need
for medical and psychiatric care.

TREATMENT

Heroin addicts—who live on the edges of death from disease, accident, homicide, or suicide—have a most uncertain and precarious
existence.   Their efforts to stay clean routinely fail.   A few will
actually not resume shooting or sniffing heroin after one or another
of their attempts at abstinence.   The concept of the "maturing
out" of addicts may apply occasionally.   Involved here are people
in their forties who stop because their emotional needs and drives
have diminished—the "burnt-out" addicts.   Unknown numbers
undergo some stabilization of their maintenance dose and will
continue to use the drug without increasing it.   These may be
affluent individuals or those who have a reliable connection with
relatively clean material and can "score" whenever necessary.   An
increasingly large group is becoming deaddicted in one of a variety

of promising programs. The rest die addicted from the diseases of
addiction, by violence, or from some intercurrent illness.

The classical approach of federal and state narcotics centers is physical separation from the drug, group therapy, physical and vocational rehabilitation, and close follow-up of the committed addict.
After release, urine tests for opium alkaloids or Nalline tests are
done at random intervals to detect the presence of heroin in the
system. They can demonstrate usage within the past 72 hours.
Nalline is a morphine analogue which does not produce euphoria,
but will induce withdrawal symptoms and dilation of heroin-con-
stricted pupils within a half hour.

Synanon is an operation which is run by clean addicts, and successfully deaddicts those dope fiends (as they are called at Synanon)
who have the motivation to stay with the program. It involves a
realistic group encounter therapy in which the addict has little
chance of conning ex-addicts with his rationalizations and self-pity.
Hundreds of former addicts have successfully made it for five years
and more with the help of Synanon.

Daytop Lodge, Narcotics Anonymous, Teen Challenge, and a number of church groups all have had some success in demonstrating
that "Once a hype, always a hype" is untrue. Exodus House is a
halfway house that takes the imprisoned addict through a series
of stages till he can live independently without drugs.

Another promising approach to the treatment of heroin dependence is the use of methadone and cyclazozine. Methadone, an
addicting drug, is given by mouth and blocks the mental effect of
heroin. Cyclazozine is an analgesic and is considered a physiological antagonist to heroin which does not induce craving. Both
drugs are supposed to diminish the effect of heroin and the desire
for it. Addicts in studies where they are used are seen daily and
checked for clandestine narcotics usage. Obviously, these are a

special group of motivated addicts who want to do something about their addiction.

The number of heroin users has been decreasing during the past quarter century. It is hoped that this trend will continue. There are signs, however, that a ready-made market for heroin is being formed from the increasing numbers who are involved in the lesser drugs of abuse.

THE SEDATIVES

The sedatives are an ancient group of plants to which have been added modern synthetic members of considerable potency. The procurement of sleep and the relaxation of the day's tensions have been sought since the cavemen. Today, quietude or temporary oblivion is most frequently obtained with the barbiturates. Barbital, the first of a long series of barbiturates, was introduced 65 years ago. The longer-acting phenobarbital and the shorter-acting Nembutal, Seconal, and Amytal are the barbiturates which are most often misused. Tuinal, an Amytal-Seconal combination, has also come into nonmedical use.

Any sedative can be abused; in addition to the barbiturates, Doriden, bromides, and chloral have been taken to excess. Although the tranquilizers are a group apart, they, too, produce oversedation or drunkenness when abused. Miltown is an example of a minor tranquilizer which has attracted a few devotees.

The sedatives have important medical uses, such as the induction of sleep, daytime calming, and the treatment of epilepsy. Some are excellent anesthetics when injected. They are often used in small doses along with other drugs for a variety of psychosomatic conditions, such as high blood pressure, peptic ulcers, and spastic colitis. Not infrequently, a patient who temporarily requires sedatives for sleep is overconcerned about becoming addicted. He may refuse such medication or, if he does accept, worry about taking one or two sleeping pills in a night. This is a needless concern. If the insomniac, himself, raises the dose above three or four capsules, he approaches the problematic level and should deal with the sleep question with his physician. Drugs are generally quite unnecessary to procure a good night's rest. When they are used, they should be taken intermittently rather than continuously. A skillful physician and his patient can often work out a program of procuring sleep without sedatives or with minimal amounts of sleeping pills. Fear of not sleeping is sometimes more of a problem than the insomnia itself.

In some instances barbiturates and other sedatives are misused by a physician. He may not supervise the patient sufficiently. He may not examine the basis for the complaints the symptoms of which he is treating. The doctor may yield to the patient's demand for increased amounts of the drug when, in fact, the patient is manifesting tolerance to the sedative. He may prescribe large amounts of the agent and permit multiple prescription refills without periodic checks to determine whether proper use is being made of them. The physician should maintain the same reservations about the accuracy of the barbiturate user's history as he does about the alcoholic's. Chronic drug users tend to minimize their intake either out of shame or because they hope for further supplies. The chronically intoxicated person who lacks the odor of alcohol could be a barbiturate habitué.

More frequently the barbiturates are obtained illicitly and swallowed to withdraw from life's difficulties or to feel less tense. Some use barbiturates to lose their inhibitions and act out what is ordinarily repressed. They are also used to take the jagged edge off a large pep-pill habit.

"Goofballs" appear in the marketplace in a variety of colored capsules, less frequently as tablets, and rarely in multidose vials for injection. The "pillhead" often derives a nickname for them according to their color. Seconals are "red devils," Nembutals are "yellow jackets," Tuinals are "rainbows," and Amytal capsules are "blue angels." A frequently used combination is a barbiturate with an amphetamine. Dexamyl in America and Drinamyl in England are examples of marketed combinations of Dexedrine and Amytal. Although these two groups of drugs are antagonists, they do not completely neutralize each other. Instead, they may calm without making the individual sleepy or stimulate without producing the jitteriness produced by Dexedrine alone. Abuse of sedative-stimulant combinations is well known. Large numbers of these capsules are taken daily. The long-term complications combine the undesirable aspects of both classes of drugs.

Another not uncommon combination is that of alcohol and barbiturates. Since alcohol is chemically and pharmacologically an anesthetic, the sedative qualities of barbiturates are potentiated. This can result in an unexpected degree of incoordination, intoxication, or coma. Occasionally a person will die in his sleep, and his blood will be found to contain amounts of alcohol and barbiturates which separately were less than sufficient to cause death. Such instances probably are not suicides, but accidental deaths resulting from the combined effect of sublethal amounts of the two drugs. This hazard is particularly liable to be met by drinkers who have quantities of sleeping pills on hand for insomnia. On the other hand, a few people who are intent on suicide will get drunk on alcohol to work up the courage to take a handful of "sleepers."

In addition to the simultaneous use of drugs, the serial use of many classes of drugs is amply documented. Individuals who take a bemusing assortment of chemicals together or in series have been called "multihabituated." Their problem might well be called "the Hell's Angel syndrome." They may go on a goofball binge, then "turn on" with one or more of the psychedelics, "fly high" with the amphetamines or certain reducing pills, dabble with a few "pops" of heroin, and then drink themselves into a stupor with whiskey. Obviously, this pharmacological medley can be catastrophic, but a few people make it a way of life.

Intoxication with sedatives is reminiscent of alcohol drunkenness. A staggering gait, slurred speech, and poor coordination are acute signs of overdosage. Ordinarily drowsiness, inability to concentrate, impaired memory, and gross defects in judgment will occur in the person who has taken more than his limit. Naturally, sleep intervenes if the person permits himself to rest.

Paradoxically, many misusers of sedatives are overexcited and restless and manifest wide mood swings. They may speak of being "up," not "down" as one might predict. This is the equivalent to the excitation of the alcoholic. Barbiturism may be present as a delirious state with confusion, loss of orientation, hallucinations, and paranoid delusions.

Chronic barbiturate usage produces tolerance within a short period. The development of the requirement to take large amounts in order to achieve the desired state of either calming or a high is not as pronounced as with the opiates and the stimulants.

The sorts of people likely to become overinvolved in sleeping pills are:

    1 The alcohol addict in an effort to exceed the effects of drinking alone, in fighting off the DTs, or when trying to dry out.

    2 The narcotic addict when his supplies are cut off or when he

wants to to intensify the awayness of heroin. It is not uncommon to obtain a history from a "junkie" including the fact
that he has also been addicted to barbiturates during his career on heroin.

3 Students with an underlying personality disturbance or situational problem with considerable anxiety, where quantities of
sleeping pills are available.

4 Anxiety-ridden or depressed individuals who are unable to
sleep or tolerate the waking state and are willing to regulate
their own medication.

5 Patients who, without supervision, have been allowed to increase their sedative intake to the point of dependence.

6 Binge users who use barbiturates just as others have lost weekends with alcohol.

7 Those dependent on amphetamines who become too agitated
on their basic drug and use barbiturates to quiet them down.

8 The multihabituated psychopath who will take barbiturates
along with, or instead of, any other drug.

Poisoning is always a danger in chronic users. The barbiturate
taker may be so confused that he may overdose himself, not re-
membering that he has taken previous doses. Even patients taking sleeping medication under a doctor's care may keep repeating
their dose on a particularly restless night and achieve toxic levels.

A definite abstinence syndrome is seen in barbiturate addicts
within a day of abrupt removal from their drug. It can be strenuous and severe, sometimes more impressive than heroin withdrawal. The "shakes," which are due to anxiety and muscle
spasms, the "fits," which are major convulsions, and the "horrors,"
which involve terrifying hallucinations and deluded thinking—all
may be present. The patient may not be able to eat, or to retain
food if he does. He returns wakeful and panicky and may run a
high fever. As with alcoholic DTs, death is possible for run-down
patients. Nondrinkers who develop DTs should be suspected of
being in a barbiturate withdrawal state.

The dangers of chronic barbiturism are manifold. Death from overdosage has been mentioned. The intoxicated state leads to accidents to the person or those around him. Chronic barbiturate users are particularly accident-prone. Barbiturates are the most commonly employed chemical mode of committing suicide. Mixing a sedative with other sedatives, tranquilizers, or other depressants can lead to a lethal coma. The loss of recent memory of the befogged barbiturate user has resulted in gross errors of judgment and fatal accidents. It is often difficult to state what will constitute a fatal dose. As few as eight capsules each containing 100 mg (milligrams) of a moderately rapid-acting barbiturate have caused death in sensitive persons; thirty capsules are almost invariably fatal. Death is usually due to respiratory arrest. On the other hand, individuals who have achieved tolerance have swallowed more than fifty capsules a day, every day, and survived.

The treatment for acute or chronic sedative overdosage requires hospitalization; and at times such heroic measures as the use of the artificial kidney, the respirator, and the cardiac stimulator may be necessary. Abrupt barbiturate withdrawal may not be safe, for death has occurred under such circumstances. Gradual reduction is safer, or the substitution of another sedative or tranquilizer.

Sedative dependence is a chronic relapsing disorder. In this sense, too, it resembles alcohol dependence. The drug may be removed from the system, but if substantial changes are not made in the personality of the patient, his life situation, or his social milieu, he will slip back into drug taking again.

What has been said about the barbiturates applies equally to all other sedatives except the bromides. Acute bromism is rare, but chronic bromide intoxication remains an occasional problem. This results from overuse of patent medicines which contain bromides. The bromides slowly accumulate in the tissues, and eventually this leads to depression, sluggishness, and delirium. Headache is often a symptom of bromism, and the complaint leads to the additional use of bromides for the relief of headache. Treatment consists of washing bromides out of the system with chlorides, usually salt solution.

THE STIMULANTS
& COCAINE

CHAPTER EIGHT

STIMULANTS

The stimulants are essentially those drugs in the amphetamine group. Other "uppers" include Ritalin, Meretran, Preludin, and a few other drugs that are used to reduce appetite and therefore weight. The most common amphetamine stimulants are Benzedrine ("bennies"), Dexedrine ("dexies"), and Methedrine ("speed," "meth," or "crystal"). The entire group is also called "pep pills" or "jolly beans."

Their medical indications include the treatment of mild depressions, narcolepsy, obesity, and certain behavioral disorders of children. They have a temporary usefulness in preventing sleep on those occasions where sleep is undesirable. Their use is not recommended as a routine procedure, but only under emergency conditions.

Occasional instances of giving stimulants to athletes to improve their performance and endurance have been recorded. This is possible when a transient extreme effort must be made. Motor performance may be enhanced, but judgment is impaired, and instances are known where athletes overtaxed their hearts when the warning signs of exhaustion were masked by stimulants.

The occasional, supervised, low-dosage use of these drugs to elevate mood and induce a state of well-being is quite safe. The student who takes a Dexedrine tablet to stay alert and study for an exam is not to be compared to the person who makes a career out of Dexedrine taking. Its continuous use is perilous, for tolerance and psychic dependence develop within weeks. It is common for an apathetic depression to occur after discontinuing the prolonged use of amphetamines. As a result amphetamines are restarted by the patient. The results of tolerance are astonishing. As much as 1,000 mg of Dexedrine, one hundred times the average dose, may be injected by the long-term user. This much no longer elevates his blood pressure, dilates his pupils, or produces a hyperexcited state as might be assumed. All that may be noted is some anxiety, jitteriness, wakefulness, and a dry mouth. Over the long term this sort of dependence leads to physical and mental problems. Malnutrition and debilitation due to self-neglect eventually appear. An aura of suspiciousness pervades the thinking of the user, and he often acts upon it. Paranoid schizophrenia is the end stage of this thinking disorder and is a well-known complication of prolonged amphetamine abuse. The visual or auditory hallucinations and the delusional thought content experienced by some people may persist long after the drug has been discontinued. Other people become panicky and experience a flight of fanciful ideas, hypersensitivity to stimuli, and a manicky inability to stop pacing or talking. These breakdowns may last only a few days, but it is not uncommon for a preschizophrenic to decompensate into a prolonged psychosis following amphetamine abuse. Depressive psychoses are also known after discontinuing amphetamines, and suicides are a hazard during this period.

True physical withdrawal effects such as those seen with barbiturates or opiates are not encountered. In this respect the stimulants resemble the psychedelics and cocaine. Extreme lethargy, fatigue, sleepiness, and mental depression are the prominent symptoms.

For amphetamine-dependent individuals, especially those who take the drug intravenously, abstinence is most difficult. Many would like to get off their stimulant, but few can succeed. The "high" is so enticing and the amphetamine-free period is so "low" that these patients are not easy to treat outside a mental hospital. Sometimes they require legal commitment to a closed facility. During the rocky course of their dependence, their excitability and poor judgment combine to make their behavior assaultive, antisocial, or unpredictable. In later stages, the excitement and derangement of mental activity become difficult to endure. They turn to barbiturates or opiates to take the edge off their tense euphoria.

The truck driver who wants to drive through weariness, the tired housewife who likes the lift her reducing pills offer, the drug-oriented teen-ager who will try anything once—these are people vulnerable to a driving accident or to a career of amphetamine dependence. If they happen to be emotionally inadequate or schizoid, the risks are greater. Naturally, a poor life situation adds to the attraction of uppers. Prisoners consumed the contents of Benzedrine nasal inhalers until the manufacturer changed the material to a nonamphetamine vasoconstrictor. The attractions of pep pills are their "superthinking" powers, an invigorating freshness, and the keenness of perceptions that is felt. New and wondrous insights are claimed, either personal or philosophic.

As an example of how situational and personal factors can combine to produce an epidemic of amphetamine addiction, the Japanese experience can be cited. After World War II the collapse of the traditional culture and the difficulties of earning a living with a single job provided the setting for a new habit, amphetamine misuse. It was at this time that large military supplies of the drug were released to commercial outlets. It is estimated by those who surveyed the situation in urban areas like Kurume that 5 percent of those between fifteen and twenty-five years of age were psychically dependent on Methedrine. Many paranoid psychoses were reported as due to the mass amphetamine misuse. Stricter controls over the drug led to an improvement in the numbers involved. In 1954 alone, the Japanese police arrested 55,000 abusers of amphetamines. However, the pattern of juvenile stimulant abuse continues to the present.

Special mention must be made of one amphetamine, Methedrine. Methedrine abuse is on the rise in this country, particularly among the youngsters who live in hippie colonies or are weekend hippies. It is popular in our hip subculture, and it is often taken with LSD. Instances are known in which LSD has been abandoned in favor of sniffing or "mainlining" meth, or speed, every few hours. The thrill, or "flash," that follows soon after the intravenous Methedrine injection must be very similar to the feeling of nongenital orgasm following cocaine injection. Like cocaine, Methedrine provides a mind-accelerating high during which activity rather than passivity can occur. The activity may be orderly, repetitive, or chaotic. Sexual interest may be enhanced or diminished. Hunger pangs and interest in food are so reduced that an experienced "methhead" forces himself to eat. Otherwise, malnutrition or even cachexia (serious weakness and emaciation) develops among Methedrine-dependent persons. Sleeplessness may be so prolonged during a Methedrine binge that it contributes to the psychotic breakdowns which occasionally follow prolonged use.

Ritalin is a nonamphetamine stimulant which can cause a clinical picture similar to that caused by speed. Since Methedrine and Dexedrine are easier to obtain, Ritalin will probably never become a widespread problem drug. A few people have become deeply involved in Ritalin overuse both orally and intravenously.

Even in the Hashbury district of San Francisco, one of the many posters in a poster-loving community says, "Speed kills." And it can. "Speedfreaks" on two hundred to a thousand times the average dose of speed lose interest in food or body care. Abscesses develop at injection sites. They heal poorly because of impaired health. In fact, all the dangers of "skin popping" and "mainlining" are present when speed, heroin, or any other substance is injected carelessly. An unsterile needle, syringe, or vial can introduce bacteria into the bloodstream (bacteremia), some with a predilection to lodge on the heart valve (subacute bacterial endocarditis). Other infections can be introduced: tetanus, syphilis, malaria, or viral hepatitis. There is some evidence to indicate that enormous doses of Methedrine can, over time, injure brain cells. Brain-wave changes can persist for months after amphetamine withdrawal. We do know that the speedster, with his potential for violence, paranoia, physical depletion, bizarre behavior —and a life which centers on speed—is in a desperate chemical maze without a visible way out. About 40 percent of the "acidheads" we interview have been or are deeply involved with speed.

COCAINE

It is almost unnecessary to deal with cocaine abuse today, especially when focusing on the student population. However, cocaine is beginning to make a comeback now that a ready-made market for chemical ecstasy exists. It has no medical use, since synthetics have been developed that exceed it in effectiveness as a local anesthetic without producing some of its side effects. It is available in a few North African, European, and Middle Eastern cities. The smuggling of cocaine across our national boundaries is not great, but very recent seizures at points of entry in New York, Los Angeles, and New Orleans indicate a modest renewed effort to reestablish the cocaine trade. Cocaine has recently been a negligible factor in drug misuse, except among heroin users and isolated hipsters who will try anything. But since some of its history is illuminating to the general drug problem and it is predictable that its use will increase, it is worthy of brief consideration.

The leaves of the coca shrub (*Erythroxylon coca*) have been chewed for at least three millennia by dwellers in villages high in the Andes, where before the Spanish conquest, the Incas used them during religious ceremonies. About 90 percent of the males and 20 percent of the women who live in the rarefied atmosphere of the Peruvian and Bolivian highlands of the Andes chew about 1 oz. of the limed leaves daily. The leaves provide them with an antifatigue, antihunger, and anticold substance that sustains them through a life of toil and deprivation.

Interestingly, although the plant grows down in the foothills, the lowlanders are rarely involved with coca-leaf chewing. When the Andean comes down to live at sea level, he usually (though not always) gives up the habit. In these instances the usage seems predominantly situationally determined; a dependence is based upon a really harsh and stressful 2-mile-high existence.

Cocaine is an extreme illustration of the mistaken idea that if a drug is not physically addictive, it has no grave, harmful effects. Cocaine does not produce physical dependence; that is, tolerance does not occur, nor do withdrawal effects. Nevertheless, the psychic craving is very strong because cocaine is a potent stimulant, excitant, and euphoriant. Traditionally, "snow" has been sniffed, occasionally resulting in perforations of the nasal septum. Today, the confirmed cocainist prefers intravenous injections. He may "shoot" the drug as often as three or four times an hour because the thrilling, ecstatic effect appears immediately but disappears quickly, too. The psychic effects are reminiscent of the psychedelics, with orgasmic highs, elation, colorful hallucinations, and feelings of peaceful bliss all described. A sense of freedom from all restraint and paranoid notions of omnipotence are also familiar to those who know the state. The effects of large amounts of Methedrine resemble the effects of cocaine.

The high is so high that eventually the user tends to modulate the state with a "downer." The favorite combination is the "speedball," an intravenous injection of heroin and cocaine. The modern speedball happens to be an intravenous mixture of LSD and Methedrine.

In earlier days a number of doctors, including Sigmund Freud, considered cocaine to be a most useful agent. He described its "energizing, exhilirating. liberating effects" and recommended it to his colleagues and his fiancée. He suggested its use for melancholia. It was, perhaps, the psychedelic of 75 years ago, for it expanded the mind and intensified sexual activities, the same claims made for LSD and Methedrine. It took years before medical men became aware of the intense craving and the subsequent physical depletion that developed. Some of the side effects are headache, nausea, vomiting, and a peculiar feeling as though insects were crawling over the skin.

Preoccupation with obtaining and using cocaine leads to indifference to health, loss of appetite, and emaciation; its frequent use leads to convulsions. When death occurs, it is because of paralysis of the breathing center in the brain.

THE SNIFFERS

CHAPTER NINE

THE ANESTHETICS

The historical antecedents of our present-day sniffers were the venerable anesthetic inhalers. It is remarkable that all three of the original general anesthetics—ether, chloroform, and nitrous oxide—were used as intoxicating agents even before they were known to be anesthetics. As noted earlier, during the nineteenth century, chloroform parties were held at Cambridge University and elsewhere until its toxicity became evident. The safer ether was more widespread as a source of fun. For a while in Ireland ether threatened to displace alcohol. Ether frolics were well known: "The students at Harvard used to inhale sulfuric ether from their handkerchiefs, and it intoxicated them and made them reel and stagger." W. T. G. Morton, "A Memoir to the Academy of Sciences at Paris on a New Use of Sulphuric Ether," *Littel's Living Age*, 529–571 (March 18), 1848.

Even more widespread was the use of laughing gas, or nitrous oxide. College students, writers, high society, and those who were willing to spend a quarter at county-fair laughing gas exhibitions all discovered the delightful and hilarious inebriation. This mundane anesthetic, now administered for dental extractions and minor surgery, is of interest to us for historical and current reasons. First, it was the primary nineteenth-century psychedelic. Some of the descriptions of its effects rival those of today's reports of chemical psychedelic encounters. William James, whose *Varieties of Religious Experience* remains a classic, considered nitrous oxide to be a mind-expanding substance.

Consider the following anonymous report:

> I have reached infinity. I have been able to dissociate myself from this world. Life on earth becomes a fleeting split-second memory in the realm of the universe. During one session I was conscious of the fact that if I really wanted to find the answers to life, I would have to die. And I am convinced that I could have died if I wanted to pursue my search further. My body would eventually be suspended, completely dissociated from this world in a Godlike state. Under withdrawal of the substance, atoms, sound, and light rapidly fell back into place like a jigsaw puzzle, revealing to my great astonishment and disappointment the reality of this life and this world, which had just been no more than a tiny segment, a remote memory on this greater world of which I was privileged to be a part. These experiences were actually religious in spite of the fact that I am not religious at all.

This is an extract of some notes taken after a dental procedure employing laughing gas.

Currently an occasional young person is found to be a laughing-gas inhaler. Cylinders and aerosols of the gas are available from hospital-supply dealers and even more widely from industry. It is used as a whipped-cream propellant, for the ignition of racing cars, and in other industrial processes. It is therefore widely and easily available. In the coming years more people may rediscover this agent.

THE VOLATILE SOLVENTS

Very low in the hierarchy of those who chemically manipulate their consciousness are the sniffers. They are low in status, belong to the lowest economic class, and achieve a mental state of low order with little to recommend it.

The products that they have at their disposal are model-airplane glue, lighter fluid, gasoline, and certain nail-polish removers. Chemically, these consist of xylene, toluene, benzene, and acetone in varying amounts. Lighter fluid usually contains naphtha, which is somewhat less toxic than the others.

Glue sniffers are numerically the most important. Hundreds of cases are seen yearly by the juvenile authorities of any large city. In 1963 over 2,000 cases were reported to juvenile authorities in this country. Smaller communities with a substantial underprivileged group may witness an occasional epidemic of inhaling airplane "dope." Most studies reveal a large proportion of males, some as young as eight, with a mean age of about fourteen. Glue is obtainable not only in toy and hobby shops but also in candy stores and supermarkets.

A severely disorganized home life is almost invariably found. Delinquent parents and siblings or homes without fathers are predisposing factors. The glue sniffers are introduced to the habit by their peers. The easy availability of the tubes of liquid airplane cement which can be shoplifted makes it a convenient intoxicant. Petty theft of other merchandise helps pay for the glue when it is kept out of reach by the proprietor. Truancy, running away from home, and antisocial behavior coexist with, or are caused by, the airplane-glue intoxication. Violent or erratic activities, car accidents, serious falls, and assaultiveness are amply documented. What is sought in the "unglued," intoxicated state is a relief from daily tensions and a period of euphoria or away-ness.

Commonly, the contents of a tube are squeezed into a small plastic bag, which is then pressed against the nose and mouth. In that manner a high concentration of the volatile solvent can be achieved. Another technique is to place a large plastic bag over one's head in order to retain the fumes. Both practices can be deadly. Asphyxiation is a well-known complication. The light-headed euphoria can proceed to a bemused delirium and terminate in a coma from which one may never recover if access to air is closed off. Other effects include ringing in the ears, double vision, a staggering gait, and convulsion-like body movements.

Although sniffing is primarily a practice of youngsters at the grade school and junior high school levels, recently a few adults have ventured into the sniffing scene. They belong to the growing band of hedonists and escapists who will try anything at least once. Although a whole array of deliriants and psychedelics is available to them, they still want to explore every high, including the glue high.

In addition to the dangers already mentioned, the persistent use of glue can damage the bone marrow and liver. Anemia is the most common manifestation of chronic toxicity, but not the only one. All the volatile solvents will produce irritation of the eyes, the nose, and the lining of the respiratory system.

The sniffing of gasoline and lighter fluid follows a similar age, sex, and class distribution. These fluids are generally poured on rags and sniffed until dizziness, incoordination, and confusion occur. Gasoline is the most readily available of all the volatile solvents, but its unpleasant odor and nauseating tendencies make it less attractive. Chronic gasoline sniffers should be checked for lead poisoning.

Amyl nitrite needs only mention, for it is an infrequent form of sniffing abuse. It is marketed in a frangible ampule covered with a silk net. When a patient with angina pectoris feels chest pain, he breaks the ampule and inhales the contents. Like nitroglycerin, amyl nitrite dilates the coronary blood vessels. A few adolescents have found that inhaling amyl nitrite is a brief intoxicant. One tale is that it is inhaled at the moment of orgasm.

The latest twist in the sniffer's saga is the breathing of Freon aerosol spray. Freon is a fluorinated hydrocarbon used as a refrigerant and propellant for a wide variety of medicaments, insecticides, and other active agents. A few venturesome souls have inhaled deeply of the liquid and have achieved unconsciousness. In itself Freon is probably nontoxic and nonintoxicating. What apparently happens when a sufficient concentration is inhaled is that it excludes oxygen from the lungs. The resulting lack of oxygen causes lightheadedness, stupor, and eventually coma. The experience is a form of partial suffocation.

The use of crude intoxicants among children is a symptom of a much greater social problem—that of the emotionally unstable or deprived youngster. This problem cannot be adequately considered here. Measures to prevent indulgence in the intoxicating solvents would logically be imbedded in a school health and safety program dealing with other hazardous household products. The problem of the habitual sniffer is not always easily correctable because of the associated familial and personal difficulties. Sometimes, removal from the disruptive environment is necessary. One positive and simple step is stricter controls on the availability of airplane glues and similar substances to the adolescent. A number of communities have taken legal action to make the volatile solvents more difficult for the subteen-ager to obtain.

THE "HEAD"

CHAPTER TEN

IDENTIFICATION

Before a person becomes a "head," the early recognition of his involvement with drugs may avoid progression to promiscuous overuse. The early signs of abuse in the student are not easily identified. When the individual is seen while under the influence, the physical effects are rarely marked. The amphetamines, the psychedelics, and cocaine dilate the pupils of the eye, sometimes to the point where they will not react to a light. They also may cause marked weight loss. The hard-narcotics user has constricted, sometimes "pinpoint" pupils. Dark glasses may be worn to conceal these changes. Other physical signs are sparse—the flushed face of the person on an LSD trip, the lingering characteristic odor of the marihuana or glue user. Stimulants sometimes produce irritability and overactivity. Large doses cause a dry mouth and lips which require repetitive licking movements. Barbiturates and opiates can make people sleepy, "on the nod." Large amounts of barbiturates and similar medicines produce a staggering gait and poor coordination, and may lead to cigarette or "reefer" burns. All the drugs that alter mood and behavior can intoxicate, confuse, and dull. The bedrugged state is one of the possibilities to consider whenever odd, disturbed, or stuporous periods occur in a person ordinarily well-behaved. On the other hand, small amounts permit the user to pull himself together and perform naturally.

In the sober interval between drug exposures, fresh needle marks or, later, "tracks" of old hypodermic-needle scars can be seen along the course of veins. "Skin poppers" may have infections or healed abscess scars on the thighs, abdomen, or arms. Sniffers can have inflammations of the eyes, nose, or throat. "Snorters" of cocaine or Methedrine are liable to develop nasal tissue damage. Withdrawal effects simulating the flu may be witnessed. Blood and urine tests are available for most of the abused substances.

More revealing than the direct effects of drug overusage are the sometimes striking changes in personality and interest patterns. School attendance becomes irregular, grades drop, and study is neglected. With the going street rate of LSD at $5 a capsule, heroin at $5 to $10 a dose, sleepers and amphetamines at about 25 cents a pill, and reefers from 25 cents and up, the financial requirements soon become formidable. A $50-to-$100-a-day heroin habit is by no means unknown. The other drugs are less of a monetary strain, but they exceed most allowances, and frequent requests for money are made. Alternatively, money or household items may be stolen, or the youngster may resort to shoplifting.

A reversal of the waking-sleeping pattern is well known. The drug abuser goes out at night and sleeps during the day. Weekends are spent with drug-using friends. This pattern of association with dubious characters and loss of interest in previous friends, along with a withdrawal from the family, is behavior that requires explanation. These indirect changes are not in themselves evidence of drug misuse, but they sometimes accompany it. They require an explanation of the situation by talks with the young person, not accusations.

The confirmed head is much more readily identifiable than the occasional user. He either willingly proclaims his involvement or is careless about concealing the evidence of misuse. In dress, talk, and behavior he deviates from his previous standards. The drug is now his central focus; all other plans and transactions are subservient to the bedrugged state.

PERSONALITY

Drug fashions come and go, though one or two will remain with the culture. But the person vulnerable to becoming overdependent on external agents is always with us. Many might try the drugs of the day; then most pass on to other life activities. A few remain dependent upon one potion or another. Why?

It is all too easy to speak of "the addictive personality." Surely, such people can be described, but they are not of a single personality configuration. Other factors are equally important in the drug-personality relationship, and the entire interaction must be examined. What must be remembered is that many youngsters with a so-called addictive personality profile are not, and will not become, dependent on drugs.

One kind of person who may have difficulties with drugs is the emotionally immature person. Usually he is passive and dependent in his dealings with others. Dealing with life situations is unduly frustrating and anxiety-provoking. He tends to lean on others or withdraw from active involvement as much as possible. His every attempt to be outgoing results in further rebuffs, he thinks, and thus in more hostility, which he expresses passively or less frequently in impulsive outbursts. He can become very angry as a result of the rejections, real or imagined, but rarely dares to show it. Rather, he bewails his misfortunes, blames others for his failings, or becomes depressed. He is quite sensitive to his inadequacies, his helplessness, and his inability to cope. It is obvious what a drug habit does for such a person. He loses his timidity and inhibitions, gains courage, and imagines himself a more powerful figure, while fantasies of achievement and creativity erase the shortcomings of a lifetime. The drug, whether it be sedative or stimulant, narcotic or psychedelic, has provided a temporary sense of adequacy and imperturbability which he never enjoyed while sober. It also solves his problem of dealing with the aggressive and sexual feelings which are threatening for him to express. It is no wonder that he comes to lean heavily on the drug and to insist that it has solved his hang-ups.

Another good candidate for a career of drug dependence is the impulse-ridden, angry young man who will try anything once— and does. He characteristically has problems with authority, and a fringe benefit of illicit drug usage for him is the fact that he is defying the law. Some such people are psychopaths; they have no conscience and little concern for others except, perhaps, for their gang. They act out when they are unlikely to get caught, and drugs or alcohol allows further loss of control and further aberrant behavior.

Then there is the borderline personality, not psychotic, but somehow strange, a bit bizarre in his thinking, shy and seclusive, unable to communicate easily. You have the peculiar feeling that a glass partition is interposed between him and you and that genuine, warm contacts are not possible. He also senses this differentness, and he searches for that which will make him more like other people. Drugs may briefly remove the partition, and they are therefore attractive and important to him. Not only this person, whom psychiatrists call "schizoid," but many other young people have real troubles handling their person-to-person relationships. Drugs and drink dissolve the inhibitions.

Depressed, tormented, and alienated people may seek a magical surcease via drugs. Many complain of being empty, unable to feel. Or they are apathetic, without energy, always tired. To feel with intensity, to feel alive, is a new and wonderful experience for them. These existentially lost people find in mind-altering drugs enjoyment and fun, which others know in the sober state.

It is people in these categories who are likely to become entwined in some drug habit. In addition, individuals having quite stable character structures can become heavily involved if their life situation is deplorable—or if they think it is. Those in physical or psychic discomfort, the discouraged, and the hopeless are apt to use chemicals to assuage actual or imagined distress.

The adolescent has a special susceptibility to involvement with drugs. In addition to the normal exploratory behavior of youth and a sense of bravado, he is under the pressures of peer-group enticement. If his friends are users, it is difficult for him to resist their persuasions even if he wishes to do so. In such instances a so-called friend is really a fellow's enemy. Peer-group interactions are generally marked by mimicking the worst behavior rather than the best. When familial and societal restraints are lacking and the growing youngster has not yet developed the cautionary attitudes of a future-oriented person, even a stable young man may become overinvolved with drugs. The drive-suppressing effects of most abused psychochemicals are especially attractive to those who have greatest difficulty in handling them—the young. The passive state where all drives are satiated or neutralized with drugs and the striving is stilled has great attractions. True, the solution is temporary and emotional maturation has halted, but the experience is satisfactory while it lasts.

SITUATIONAL FACTORS

It is possible to distinguish at least a dozen situations in which individuals vulnerable to becoming dependent on drugs will become overinvolved with one or more of the habituating drugs:

1 The severely inadequate, the immature, the lost and depressed, the prepsychotic, and the psychotic have already been mentioned. They all seek a simple, quick, magical solution to their character defects. Little urging is needed to get them started, and it is most difficult for them to put down the habit once it has been fixed.

2 Then there are the curious ones willing to take a chance. If simple curiosity is the major reason for trying a drug, they rarely become heads. Curiosity is not infrequently given as an excuse for starting a habit when, in fact, some character defect perpetuates the drug taking.

3 The joyriders are a large segment of the head population. Their sober life situation is dismal, or they believe it to be. They cannot enjoy without chemical assistance; and once they find pharmacological pleasure, the nondrug state becomes even more intolerable. Thus "the sober certainty of waking bliss" is unknown to them, and they are very unlikely to revert to prolonged sobriety unless the bedrugged condition becomes noxious.

4 Some folk drop capsules because it is the sociable thing to do. In their set everybody is doing it. Not to do it would mean to be left out or to have nothing to talk about. Taking drugs is a prerequisite for belonging to some groups.

5 Artists have traditionally been involved with drugs for a number of reasons. They are often in spiritual pain. They are hopeful for artistic breakthroughs or for a renewal of their creative powers. They perpetually seek to spring free of the ordinary ways of seeing or sensing the world around them.

Their social restraints are generally attenuated, and illicitness is no bar to drug use.

6 "Escape" is a commonly used word when drug misuse is being described. Escape from boredom, escape from responsibility, escape from frustration, and escape from anxiety—these are real causes of drug abuse. But they do not answer more basic questions: Why boredom in this exciting world? Why avoid responsibilities when they are the stuff that helps us grow? Why so low a tolerance to frustration? Why not learn how to deal with neurotic anxiety and use the existential anxieties as a source of energy?

7 Then there are the accidental heads, those who have been "hooked" on some drug by a big brother or a friend at an age or under circumstances when they were unable to discriminate or object. These are sad situations. The reasons why an old head will turn on a person close to him are many. Some of them are the following: to derive a vicarious gratification, to control the neophyte, to give him a good time, to fulfill a sense of love or hate, or simply because misery loves company.

8 Related to the social and the accidental heads are those who have been persuaded to indulge. A husband persuades his wife; a boyfriend "turns on" the girlfriend. The head by persuasion may go along because of some misguided sense of love or because of an impression that if she were involved, she could better help her man with his drug problem. This rarely works out well.

9 Still to be mentioned are those who are subjected to extremely stressful pressures. The doctor who has to keep going, the executive who has to do the work of three, the actor who needs pills to "unwind" and pills to "rewind"—these people are candidates for becoming "rumheads," "hopheads," or "pillheads."

10 From all the above groups a growing subgroup is emerging: the chuck-wagon consumers of drugs. These people will take anything and everything, together or in sequence. What they seem to be saying by their behavior is that life has no

value and no meaning and that anything is better than this awareness.

11   On the face of it, those heads who suffer through an episode of DTs or a psychotic break following LSD or who wake up after being hauled back from death's door from an overdose of heroin might be expected to quit for good.   This happens surprisingly seldom.   They are just as likely to slip back into their old ways despite the horror and the danger of their drug experience.

12   Finally, some people become heads because they seek personal insights or religious experiences.   They are most frequently users of psychedelics.   They are searching and believe that these drugs open up new levels of awareness.   The issue of the validity of this assumption was considered in Chapter 3. It is only necessary to remind ourselves that historically alcohol, laughing gas, ether, opium, and cocaine were similarly considered to be mind expanders and were employed for this same purpose.

The availability of the drug is certainly a necessary if not a sufficient factor.   In the absence of heroin, no one ever becomes addicted to it.   With all sectors of a community exposed to a potpourri of drugs, someone will overuse them.   The best sort of control of narcotics or other dangerous drugs is at the source of supply.   In a democracy with its safeguards protecting privacy, such control is a most difficult task—but it is a price worth paying.

DRUG SPECIFICITY

The notion that some drugs promote passivity and others hyperactivity is not too well documented.   The underlying personality and the conditions under which the drug is taken seem more important than the specific drug effect.   Marihuana, the other psychedelics, and the opiates are supposed to promulgate introspection and inertia, but the opposite can and does occur. Alcohol, as is well known, can induce any sort of conduct from overactivity to complete withdrawal and from sexual aggressiveness to a complete loss of eroticism. The barbiturates, which are supposed to calm and stupefy, often excite and alert certain users. In animal studies, barbiturates given to rats caged alone decreased activity. When the same dose was given to rats in a crowded cage, it increased their activity.

The drug-personality equation must include another factor if we are to understand the current situation. That factor is the milieu, the nature of the times. Young people, as well as old, are living through a period of upheaval, multiple revolutions, and dynamic change. They have difficulty seeing clearly defined goals worth striving for and ends worth working toward. The causes that are appealing are difficult and arduous to support. They are dissatisfied with themselves, and tend to project their dissatisfactions onto the external world. Sufficient justification exists in the external world to make a case for decadence, injustice, cruelty, etc. What is forgotten, or rather what has never been learned, is that man and society have gone through innumerable cycles of construction and destruction, war and peace, growth and decay. Taking the historical perspective, one could make as good a case for hope and progress during this epoch as for the opposite. The notion that this is the worst of worlds in which to live could be easily challenged by anyone who has studied the condition of man in past generations. In fact, the opposite may be true.

However, if we feel disaffiliated, hopeless, and lonely, we are. If we happen to think that this world is not worth saving, we "drop out"—a phenomenon of great antiquity. The attraction of the new drugs which promote withdrawal and a dropped-out way of life is appealing. It is for reasons such as these that we are witnessing a period of rather widespread drug usage now. We are the victims of our ignorance, anxieties, and lack of faith.

It can be asked whether dependence on the drug groups mentioned here or upon alcohol is specific for any particular character structure. Are depressed people more likely to seek out "uppers," and do more psychopaths wind up on heroin? Although personality traits may determine the particular potion at times, the other variables are just as important. The availability of the drug, social approval or disapproval, novelty of the drug, the values and practices of the ingroup and the parents—all these and other factors may determine which drug direction one finally takes. It has been said that the opiate state is what the alcoholic is trying to achieve. The same has been said of the LSD user. The fact that some people wander from one drug habit to another indicates that various pharmacological groups will fit the needs of most people. Tension reduction and relief from depression can be obtained in a number of ways: by taking the oblivion route, by getting "high," by enjoying a lush fantasy life. We know that out of the same bottle can be poured belligerence or friendliness, happiness or sorrow, laughter or tears. The only prediction that can be ventured with some assurance is that the severe psychopath will usually wind up with the most illegal drug taken in the most antisocial manner and in the largest amounts.

The head, then, is the end result of a certain personality vulnerability, a real or presumed difficult life situation, the availability of a drug which decreases anxiety or produces euphoria—and chance.

THE DRUG DILEMMA
A PARTIAL SOLUTION

CHAPTER ELEVEN

The clichés about prevention and treatment of drug abuse are true, but hardly require repetition. Remarks such as, "Drug users are made—not born" or "Dependence on drugs is a symptom of an emotional disorder" do not help answer specific questions. An attempt will be made to go beyond the truisms with a fresh approach to today's drug-abuse problem.

THE PARENTS

One of the great myths of the day is that if a child goes wrong, becomes a drughead, for example, this must be due to parental failure. If the cause is not deprivation or neglect, it must be overprotection or possessiveness. At times it appears that the line between insufficient mothering and maternal smothering is nonexistent. This peculiar notion stems from the strong lay and professional indoctrination with the Freudian tenet that what happens in infancy determines subsequent behavior. The parents uncritically accept this thesis, and of course their children are quite willing to appropriate and elaborate on the theme that they received either too much or too little family love.

Unquestionably, substantial numbers of children are maltreated, abused, overcontrolled, or spoiled. This does not mean that they are completely incapable of overcoming these childhood handicaps. It would be both harmful and incorrect to believe that maladaptive personality patterns cannot be corrected. The individual has some responsibility in such matters. In addition, a large group of quite well-brought-up, characterologically sound children are "turned on" to drugs by their associates. It is difficult to discern how a parent can be blamed for these events. Sometimes, the parents are in a double bind. If they try to intervene, they are domineering; if they do not, they are neglectful.

Somewhere between "I don't care" and overprotection is the parental attitude which best permits the child to develop and grow up. He grows by solving problems, by learning from failure and defeat as well as from success and reward. This opportunity to become resilient by encountering and coping should not be denied any growing creature. When help is needed, the parent-child relationship ought to be so open and trusting that it is used for assistance, information, and advice. This is just as true for the issue of drug taking as for every other problem. Naturally, it would be best if drug usage could be discussed before the event, but the youngster should feel capable of talking about it afterward without fear of excessive emotionality or rejection. An open attitude need not mean acceptance of an act which the parent considers harmful. Approval is withheld, but condemnation should not be on an irrational basis. Sufficient data are at hand to point out quietly the personal, legal, and social hazards. Most often a single experience with drugs represents nothing more than the exploratory behavior of youth. If drug taking becomes habitual, it usually represents either a gratification which the young person should have been able to derive from daily living or an evasion of life experience due to inability or unwillingness to meet life's day-to-day rebuffs.

Those most attracted to drugs are those who are bored, cannot enjoy, or cannot tolerate stress and frustration. The drug fits their emotional discontent and removes the necessity to plan, to struggle, to endure. In other words, the drug abuser was usually made long before the drug appeared. Drug dependence serves to compound the individual's problem with dependence.

The parent who drinks to excess will have an impossible task in persuading his son or daughter to desist from drug usage. It is true that his act is legal and his child's is not. Nevertheless, the legality of alcoholic intoxication is not a strong argument to a child—or anyone else. Indeed, it sets an example of escapism which may be imitated.

Harsh and punitive attitudes make some children compliant, but many others rebel and become more involved in drugs as an act of defiance. Making obviously untrue statements about drugs is worse than useless. The child will tune out those who are patently trying to frighten him into desisting.

A difficult situation occurs when the young person is part of a group of drug users. Its members reinforce each other's drug taking. They become "authorities" and can outtalk parents. They may go on for some time before anything untoward happens. In such an instance a parent can hardly expect his child to abstain unless their relationship has been an unusually good one. What is more likely is that a critical moment will arise when the parent can step in and effectively help his child to stop using drugs. This moment occurs when someone in the group is hurt, someone is arrested, or someone else in the group decides to break away from the drug scene for philosophic or personal reasons.

The parent has a final responsibility which he cannot delegate to the school, the court, or the psychotherapist. However, he may have such feelings of guilt (sometimes unjustified) when his child becomes a "head" that he continues to support his offspring's deviant way of life. The parent is not necessarily guilty for a youngster's character deficit. Other people and circumstances have had powerful impacts on his character formation, too. It does not seem logical to underwrite an undesirable drug habit. Rather, the attitude should be, "I love you and I will help you, but I won't support you if you persist in behavior which I believe to be detrimental to you." Now that every large city has its "hippie" haven, this question comes up often. Regularly, parents who deplore the fact that their child has become a "druggie," has dropped out of school, and has moved off to a hippie ghetto perpetuate this sort of existence by sending him money. Often, funds from one parent will support a roomful of young people. This is unfair not only to the other youngsters but also to their parents.

Should a parent ever report a child's illegal behavior to the police or commit him for mental hospitalization? This question can only be answered on a highly individual basis. If the youngster is involved with physically addictive drugs and will not voluntarily seek help, it may become necessary to take over the decision-making responsibility. If one's offspring has become a "pusher," it may be justifiable to notify the authorities. Certainly, if he has broken with reality and has no insight into his condition, commitment to a hospital may be the only proper step. Much depends upon his age; if he is a minor, the parental responsibility is greater.

Most of the arguments which youngsters use to justify their be-drugged episodes are specious. Others are partially true, and a few are valid. If you, as a parent, set a poor example—have superficial and irrelevant goals and live according to irresponsible or inane standards—how can you hope to influence your child? The most convincing statement that can be made is your way of living. Striving for security, so important in times of hardship and poverty, is an inadequate goal during periods of relative affluence. Those of our middle-class children who do not need to struggle to obtain food and shelter find such an outmoded aspiration unacceptable. Beyond physical survival are more profound and appealing ideals. These should be sought by us and, by example, transmitted to our children. It is a feeling of existential meaninglessness which attracts some people to the drug state. The acquisition of a sense of meaningfulness is the antidote. The current problem can be seen as a disease of affluence and nondirection. For many, this generation has not found ways and means of constructively using the time formerly expended on work to evade hunger. Freedom from want has produced a vacuum of time which must be filled with meaningful activities, not time-consuming activities.

Sometimes a young "dropout" wants to drop back in after a year or two of the hippie game. The family relationship ought not to be so embittered that he cannot ask for help to find his way back. A line of communication should be available to him. Sometimes the hippie wants to come back and return to school. He will have real difficulty admitting this to himself, his friends, and his parents. At this point, the real meaning of mature love can be made clear to him. Taking him back without rancor or reproof will be an opportunity for a new beginning.

THE SCHOOL

It seems reasonable to insist that usage or trafficking of any illegal drug not be permitted on school grounds. Furthermore, psychological dependence upon mind-altering psychedelics, stimulants, sedatives, and intoxicants is contrary to the goals of the educative process, whether excessive use be on or off campus. If a place of learning is where one's intelligence, capabilities, and skills are developed and enhanced, then habitual displacement of consciousness, reality testing, and reasoning ability is antithetical to its goals. The frequent use of any drug can result in impaired performance. Indeed, a single use of some classes of drugs is associated with a temporary decrement in psychomotor functioning. Of all drug users, only those who indulge in the psychedelics claim consciousness expansion. From the observations of many who have studied this issue and from the reports of many who have gone the psychedelic route for years, chemical consciousness expansion is, in the main, a myth. The so-called revelations and enlightenments are all too often illusory. Occasionally, a valid insight may come forth, but it must be rigidly scrutinized during the sober state in order to determine its authenticity. Unfortunately, this is rarely done. Many who have acted upon psychedelic insights uncritically have met catastrophe.

If the educator is to learn anything from the current striving for drug-induced perceptual, emotional, and cognitive changes, it is that important areas of human experience have been neglected by our child-rearing and child-teaching practices. Many of those attracted to the drug experience suffer from *anhedonism*, the inability to derive pleasure from ordinary existence, and *alienation*, the inability to find meaning within or outside oneself. These are serious deficits, and in a young person they lead to serious disorders of behavior or character. From childhood through adolescence we are failing (1) to provide goals appropriate to our times, (2) to train the emotions and the senses, and (3) to set limits. Therefore, goallessness, an inability to enjoy, and an attenuated sense of social responsibility predispose to chemical escape, chemical hedonism, and the search for chemical enlightenment.

The teacher, in addition to making the educative process as interesting, constructive, and alive as possible, can also have a great influence on the decision to take or continue to take drugs. He is often the confidant when parents are lacking or have failed to accept their role. The teacher may be the first to learn of, or notice, aberrant behavior due to drugs. He may be able to persuade his pupil by presenting factual information. This is no taboo topic. If reliable information about drugs is not obtained, questionable information will be gathered from street myths.

In schools where the administration believes that no drug activity is present, there may be reluctance to rock the boat by opening up the subject. The likelihood, though, is that more drug activity is going on than comes to the awareness of the authorities. Furthermore, in users and nonusers alike, a brisk interest in the drug phenomenon is evident. Newspaper and magazine articles are read, rumors are transmitted, and considerable misinformation is exchanged. It would seem that offering to provide drug information is part of the educative process.

The teacher, as a more neutral person than the parent, can counsel or refer the student to a counselor. It is important to understand what the drug means to the student. The counselor may be able to provide better nondrug alternatives once he knows what the drug represents. A school counselor may form a group of students involved in drugs. One or more students who have passed through their drug honeymoon and have come back are very helpful in such situations.

One element that must be emphasized in all discussions about drugs is that their use is stupid, not smart or "in." The regular user even of nonaddictive drugs is in a state of maturation arrest. The drug solves his problem; he does not learn to solve problems and endure dissonance in his environment. Many drugs leave the student goofy, unable to function. This is hardly a groovy way to exist. Those drugs which are supposed to expand one's consciousness all too often fail to do so, especially if one is young and unprepared.

The growing brain is more vulnerable to all chemical agents, and temporary, perhaps even sustained harm can result. Permanent harm to the brain cells after exposure to large amounts of psychedelics is a possibility that is now undergoing intense study.

It is in peer groups that drug taking spreads. The teacher may become aware that one or a few individuals are proselytizing. An epidemic may be prevented by quick action in such instances. School authorities should make the school area a difficult place to obtain or use drugs. It is too much to expect that school authorities can be responsible for activities off the campus.

The question of confidentiality rarely comes up, but it may. If a student approaches a teacher as a friend to discuss his drug problem, he must be warned about the teacher's duties in the matter. It is to be hoped that it will be possible to listen without disclosing, but school regulations may prevent this. Under such circumstances the student must be clearly told beforehand. A certified school psychologist or psychiatrist has the advantage of being able to keep patients' statements as privileged communications. Referral to such a person will safeguard the student.

A repertoire of disciplinary measures with some built-in flexibility is preferable to rigid, mandatory punishments. The campus supplier of LSD and Methedrine is not in the same category as the youngster who has been persuaded to try a "reefer" and whose negligence has resulted in his detection. Strangely enough, the penalties for both offenses are equal—they are felonies. Unfortunately, school authorities may have no choice in the matter. They are often required to report every breach of discipline. It may be well to make students aware that a felony involves lifelong consequences beyond incarceration. This should not be done as a threat, but rather as part of setting forth the realistic here-and-now risks connected with the misuse of certain drugs.

THE THERAPIST

All too often the psychotherapist is faced with a young patient who does not want to be treated but has been forced into the office by anxious parents. Little can be done if the patient is not motivated to change. All too often he is at a phase of his drug-taking cycle when he is deriving satisfaction, euphoria, and release of tension from the chemical he is using. He is feeling no pain; what more can therapeutic intervention offer? The symptom is pleasant, the cure much less so. If his drug happens to be one of the psychedelics, he has a feeling of subjective wisdom far beyond that of the therapist. He may have a pseudo-philosophic jargon which can put many a therapist down. If, somehow, the patient cannot be motivated to examine himself and his reasons for overusing drugs, little can be accomplished. The patient is unlikely to remain in treatment, and it is the parents who should be counseled about their attitudes at this point.

Sooner or later, after a few bad trips, a psychotic break, or disillusion with the drug way of life, the devotee will want out. Perhaps it is merely that he sees the circular, pointless nature of his existence. For though an agent like LSD may be helpful in directed psychotherapy, its undirected use all too rarely has a significant psychotherapeutic impact. At this moment the skilled therapist who knows something about the nature of the psychedelic experience can perform a valuable service. The drug practices of the past months or years must be carefully examined to learn as much as possible from them. Their meaning to the patient must be uncovered and understood. Thus a bridge is built that leads the patient back into an enjoyment of this world; a reentry into this life is provided in the best possible manner. These are the most difficult of patients to treat, for they were engulfed in the psychedelic life because of their unfulfilled needs. They have tasted great gratifications in their responsibility-free, hedonistic existence. Now the therapist must help them become more responsible, find more significant goals, and begin the long, hard process of psychological maturation. The immaturity which caused them to seek the magic pill must be modified. These are valuable people, often very bright and with many contributions to make. After a period of individual therapy a psychotherapeutic group may be a place where the members can find the values of the human interaction.

THE LEGISLATOR

The control of the drugs mentioned in this book is necessary especially, but not only, for the juvenile. Passing laws can have a beneficial or a harmful effect, depending upon the wisdom of the legislation. With the current upsurge of drug misuse, especially in those of school age, it would seem reasonable to apprehend the supplier of these minors rather than to focus on catching the juvenile user or possessor. The maker, the smuggler, the pusher, and the transporter must be found and punished. The penalties for use and possession of a drug like marihuana are excessive, and excessive punishments may defeat the legislative purpose. Marihuana, a weak hallucinogen, carries penalties greater than LSD at this time. Consideration ought to be given to proposals to place marihuana on the dangerous-drug list rather than under the narcotics act as at present.

The mere passage of laws as a device to eliminate noxious behavior is an ineffective technique. The hope that a decree will abolish undesirable conduct in a democratic society is just as naïve as the expectation that a chemical potion will magically change character. In addition to sagacious laws, public education and public cooperation with the laws are needed. Somehow these must also be obtained.

THE USER

The last words are for the student or ex-student who is overinvolved in some drug—narcotic, stimulant, psychedelic, or sedative. This will be no exhortation to desist; any genuine change must start with you. Instead, let's deal as simply as possible with some of the basic questions. One question you might ask is, "What's wrong with instant joy or chemical escape?" My own answer would be, "Nothing, if it works." The trouble is that from what I have seen, "Bliss for free" doesn't work. Tolerance to pleasure seems to develop just like tolerance to drugs. This is so well known that it forms the themes of innumerable novels and movies. Constant ecstasy becomes less and less ecstatic. It eventually crumbles into nothing. Synthetic happiness satisfies, then satiates, and chemical escape is for today. What of tomorrow? Tomorrow, you may need "louder music and stronger wine" in order to fly. Tomorrow, you may need DMT in the pot, speed in the acid, a switch to the exaltation that is cocaine or to the quiet rapture of heroin. The search for the ultimate euphoria is never ending. "Pleasure now, pay later" is fine until the bills start coming in. One young man who had been through it all said it very simply, "You've got to pay your dues." If payment is delayed too long, the amount becomes staggering.

"But I can't make it without drugs, I can't get way out there or enjoy," you will say. That is your inadequacy, your immaturity. That is where you will stay if you lean on drugs. Everything that can be obtained with drugs can be accomplished without them. It means work, development, growth. The rewards are infinitely greater because you will have done it yourself. You will have paid your dues first, and the joy will be so much more genuine because it will be a reward for something you have actually accomplished. Do you want release from tensions, a feeling of joy just from being alive? Do you want to groove with people, be freer and more spontaneous? Nonchemical ways are available, but they require training and discipline. Are you willing to pay that price?

DRUG GLOSSARY

Acid	LSD, LSD-25 (lysergic acid diethylamide)
Acidhead	Frequent user of LSD (also cubehead)
Bag	Packet of drugs
Ball	Absorption of stimulants and cocaine via the genitalia
Bang	Injection of drugs
Barbs	Barbiturates
Bennies	Benzedrine, an amphetamine
Bindle	Packet of narcotics
Blank	Extremely low-grade narcotics
Blast	Strong effect from a drug
Blue angels	Amytal, a barbiturate
Blue velvet	Paregoric (camphorated tincture of opium) and Pyribenzamine (an antihistamine) mixed and injected

Bombita	Amphetamine injection, sometimes taken with heroin
Bread	Money
Bum trip	Bad experience with psychedelics
Bummer	Bad experience with psychedelics
Busted	Arrested
Buttons	The sections of the peyote cactus
Cap	Capsule
Chipping	Taking narcotics occasionally
Coasting	Under the influence of drugs
Cokie	Cocaine addict
Cold turkey	Sudden withdrawal of narcotics (from the gooseflesh, which resembles the skin of a cold plucked turkey)
Coming down	Recovering from a trip
Connection	Drug supplier
Cop out	Quit, take off, confess, defect, inform
Crystal	Methedrine, an amphetamine
Cubehead	Frequent user of LSD
Cut	Dilute drugs by adding milk sugar or another inert substance
Dealer	Drug supplier
Deck	Packet of narcotics
Dexies	Dexedrine, an amphetamine
Dime bag	$10 package of narcotics
Dirty	Possessing drugs, liable to arrest if searched
Dollies	Dolophine (also known as methadone), a synthetic narcotic
Doper	Person who uses drugs regularly
Downers	Sedatives, alcohol, tranquilizers, and narcotics
Drop	Swallow a drug
Dummy	Purchase which did not contain narcotics
Dynamite	High-grade heroin
Fix	Injection of narcotics
Flip	Become psychotic
Floating	Under the influence of drugs

Freakout	Bad experience with psychedelics; also, a chemical high
Fuzz	The police
Gage	Marihuana
Good trip	Happy experience with psychedelics
Goofballs	Sleeping pills
Grass	Marihuana
H	Heroin
Hard narcotics	Opiates, such as heroin and morphine
Hard stuff	Heroin
Hash	Hashish, the resin of Cannabis
Hay	Marihuana
Head	Person dependent on drugs
Hearts	Dexedrine tablets (from the shape)
Heat	The police
High	Under the influence of drugs
Holding	Having drugs in one's possession
Hooked	Addicted
Hophead	Narcotics addict
Horse	Heroin
Hustler	Prostitute
Hype	Narcotics addict
Joint	Marihuana cigarette
Jolly beans	Pep pills
Joy-pop	Inject narcotics irregularly
Junkie	Narcotics addict
Kick the habit	Stop using narcotics (from the withdrawal leg muscle twitches)
Layout	Equipment for injecting drug
Lemonade	Poor heroin
M	Morphine
Mainline	Inject drugs into a vein
Maintaining	Keeping at a certain level of drug effect
(The) Man	The police
Manicure	Remove the dirt, seeds, and stems from marihuana

Mesc	Mescaline, the alkaloid in peyote
Meth	Methedrine (also known as Desoxyn), an amphetamine
Methhead	Habitual user of Methedrine
Mikes	Micrograms (millionths of a gram)
Narco	Narcotics detective
Nickle bag	$5 packet of drugs
O.D.	Overdose of narcotics
On the nod	Sleepy from narcotics
Panic	Shortage of narcotics on the market
Pillhead	Heavy user of pills, barbiturates or amphetamines or both
Pop	Inject drugs
Pot	Marihuana
Pothead	Heavy marihuana user
Purple hearts	Dexamyl, a combination of Dexedrine and Amytal (from the shape and color)
Pusher	Drug peddler
Quill	A matchbook cover for sniffing Methedrine, cocaine, or heroin
Rainbows	Tuinal (Amytal and Seconal), a barbiturate combination in a blue and red capsule
Red devils	Seconal, a barbiturate
Reefer	Marihuana cigarette
Reentry	Return from a trip
Roach	Marihuana butt
Roach holder	Device for holding the butt of a marihuana cigarette
Satch cotton	Cotton used to strain drugs before injection; may be used again if supplies are gone
Score	Make a purchase of drugs
Shooting gallery	Place where addicts inject
Skin popping	Injecting drugs under the skin
Smack	Heroin
Smoke	Wood alcohol
Snorting	Inhaling drugs

Snow	Cocaine
Speed	Methedrine, an amphetamine
Speedball	An injection of a stimulant and a depressant, originally heroin and cocaine
Speedfreak	Habitual user of speed
Stash	Supply of drugs in a secure place
Stick	Marihuana cigarette
Stoolie	Informer
Strung out	Addicted
Tracks	Scars along veins after many injections
Tripping out	High on psychedelics
Turned on	Under the influence of drugs
Turps	Elixir of Terpin Hydrate with Codeine, a cough syrup
25	LSD (from its original designation, LSD-25)
Uppers	Stimulants, cocaine, and psychedelics
Weed	Marihuana
Works	Equipment for injecting drugs
Yellow jacket	Nembutal, a barbiturate
Yen sleep	A drowsy, restless state during the withdrawal period

SUMMARY OF DRUG EFFECTS

Drugs	Legal status, manufacture and sale	Legal status, possession and usage	Withdrawal symptoms	Psychological dependence	Death by overdose	Accident proneness during use	Suicidal tendencies
LSD	Felony	Misdemeanor, various state laws	No	Yes	Unknown	Yes	Yes
Marihuana	Felony	Felony	No	Yes	Unknown	Yes	Rare
Heroin	Felony	Felony	Vomiting, diarrhea, tremors, aches, sweats, etc.	Yes	Coma, respiratory failure	Yes	Yes
Barbiturates	Felony	Misdemeanor, various state laws	DTs and other symptoms	Yes	Coma, respiratory failure, shock	Yes	Yes
Amphetamines	Felony	Misdemeanor, various state laws	Depression, apathy	Yes	Convulsions, coma, cerebral hemorrhage	Yes	Yes
Cocaine	Felony	Felony	No	Yes	Convulsions, respiratory failure	Yes	Yes
Airplane glue	Various city and state laws	None, or misdemeanor by state reg.	Mild	Yes	Usually from asphyxiation	Yes	Unknown
Alcohol	Various state laws for illegal sale	Sale to minors a misdemeanor; various state laws on driving, disorderly conduct	DTs and other symptoms	Yes	Coma, respiratory failure	Yes	Yes

Physical complications	Chromosomal changes	Mental complications during use	Mental complications after use	Tolerance	Manner used	Drugs
Rare seizures, cardiovascular collapse	Yes	Panic, paranoid state	Asocial reaction, recurrences, psychoses, paranoia, anxiety reactions, brain damage?	Extremely rapid	Orally or injection	LSD
Bronchitis, conjunctivitis	Unknown	Rare panic or paranoid state	Asocial reaction, rare psychoses	Partial	Orally, by inhalation of smoke	Marihuana
Needle contamination, overdose	Unknown	Intoxication	Asocial and antisocial reactions	Yes	All mucous membranes, by injection, least effective orally	Heroin
Overdose	Unknown	Intoxication	Psychoses	Yes	Orally and by injection	Barbiturates
Malnutrition, needle contamination	Unknown	Intoxication	Paranoid psychoses, asocial reaction	Yes	Orally, sniffed, and by injection	Amphetamines
Malnutrition, perforated nose septum from sniffing	Unknown	Excited state, intoxication	Probable brain damage, paranoid psychoses	Yes	Orally sniffed, and by injection	Cocaine
Bone marrow depression, liver and kidney damage	Unknown	Excited state, intoxication	Brain damage?	Slight	Inhalation	Airplane glue
Gastritis, pancreatitis, cirrhosis, neuritis	Unknown	Intoxication	Brain damage	Partial	Orally and by injection	Alcohol

ADDITIONAL READING

GENERAL

BENDER, L., "Drug Addiction in Adolescence," *Comprehensive Psychiat.*, 4:181 (June), 1963.

DE ROPP, R. S., *Drugs and the Mind*, St. Martin's Press, Inc., New York, 1957.

DILLON, J. B., "Nitrous Oxide Inhalation as a Fad," *Calif. Med.*, 106:444 (June), 1967.

Drug Abuse: Escape to Nowhere, Smith, Kline and French Laboratories, Philadelphia, 1967.

"The Drug Takers," *Time-Life Special Report*, Time, Inc., New York, 1965.

EBIN, D. (ed.), *The Drug Experience*, Orion, New York, 1961.

EDDY, N. B., H. HALBACH, H. ISBELL, and M. H. SEEVERS, "Drug Dependence: Its Significance and Characteristics," *Bull. World Health Organ.*, 32:721–733, 1965.

GOLDSTEIN, R., *1 in 7: Drugs on Campus*, Walker and Company, New York, 1966.

GOODMAN, L. S., and A. GILMAN, *The Pharmacologic Basis of Therapeutics*, 3d ed., The Macmillan Company, New York, 1965.

KRIEG, M. B., *Green Medicine*, Rand McNally & Company, Chicago, 1964.

LEVIN, L., *Phantastica, Narcotic and Stimulating Drugs*, E. P. Dutton & Co., Inc., New York, 1964.

LINDESMITH, A. R., *The Addict and the Law*, Indiana University Press, Bloomington, Ind., 1965.

LOURIA, D., *Nightmare Drugs*, Pocket Books, Inc., New York, 1966.

White House Conference on Narcotic and Drug Abuse, GPO, Washington, 1963.

"Workshop of the Detection and Control of Abuse of Narcotics, Barbiturates and Amphetamines," U.S. Department of Health, Education, and Welfare, *Psychopharmacol. Bull.*, 3:21–62 (December), 1966.

THE PSYCHEDELICS

ABRAMSON, H. A. (ed.), *The Use of LSD in Psychotherapy and Alcoholism*, The Bobbs-Merrill Company, Inc., Indianapolis, 1967.

ALPERT, R., S. COHEN, and L. SCHILLER, *LSD*, New American Library of World Literature, Inc., New York, 1966.

BLUM, R. (ed.), *The Utopiates*, Atherton, New York, 1964.

CHOPRA, R. N., "*Cannabis sativa* in Relation to Mental Diseases and Crime in India," *Indian J. Med.*, January, 1942.

COHEN, S., *The Beyond Within: The LSD Story*, 2d ed., Atheneum Publishers, New York, 1967.

EFRON, D. H. (ed.), *Ethnopharmacologic Search for Psychoactive Drugs*, U.S. Public Health Service Publication 1045, 1967.

HOFFER, A., "D-lysergic Acid Diethylamide (LSD): A Review of Its Present Status," *Clin. Pharmacol. Therapy*, 6:183 (March–April), 1965.

HUXLEY, A., *The Doors of Perception*, Harper & Row, Publishers, Incorporated, New York, 1954.

KLÜVER, H., *Mescal and Mechanism of Hallucination*, University of Chicago Press, Chicago, 1966.

MASTERS, R. E. L., and J. HOUSTON, *Varieties of Psychedelic Experience*, Holt, Rinehart and Winston, Inc., New York, 1966.

SLOTKIN, J. S., *The Peyote Religion*, Free Press of Glencoe, New York, 1956.

SOLOMON, D. (ed.), *LSD, the Consciousness Expanding Drug*, G. P. Putnam's Sons, New York, 1964.

——— (ed.), *The Marihuana Papers*, Bobbs-Merrill, Indianapolis, 1965.

WOLSTENHOLME, G. E. W., and J. KNIGHT (eds.), *Ciba Foundation Symposium on Hashish*, Churchill, London, England, 1965.

WITCHES' BREWS AND THE LIKE

KEELER, M. H., and F. J. KANE, "The Use of Hyoscyamine as a Hallucinogen and Intoxicant," *Am. J. Psychiat.*, 124:852 (December), 1967.

MULLER, J. D., "Unpublicized Hallucinogens," *J. Am. Med. Assoc.*, 202:198 (Nov. 13), 1967.

PAYNE, R. B., "Nutmeg Intoxication," *New Engl. J. Med.*, 269:36 (July 4), 1963.

THE OPIATES

BROWN, C. T., "The Addiction Liability of Codeine," *Military Med.*, 129:1077 (November), 1964.

CHEIN, I., *The Road to H.: Narcotics, Delinquency and Social Policy*, Basic Books, Publishers, New York, 1964.

CHERUBIN, G. E., "The Medical Sequelae of Narcotic Addiction," *Ann. Internal Med.*, 67:23 (July), 1967.

COCTEAU, J. *Opium*, Grove Press, New York, 1957.

DE QUINCEY, T., *Confessions of an English Opium Eater*, Three Sirens Press, New York, 1932.

ELDRIDGE, W. G., *Narcotics and the Law*, New York University Press, New York, 1962.

FIDDLE, S., *Portraits from a Shooting Gallery*, Harper & Row, Publishers, Incorporated, New York, 1967.

HARMS, E., *Drug Addiction in Youth*, Pergamon Press, New York, 1965.

LOURIA, D. B., R. HENSLE, and J. ROSE, "Major Medical Complications of Heroin Attraction," *Ann. Internal Med.*, 67:1–22 (July), 1967.

Narcotic Drug Addiction, U.S. Public Health Service Publication 1021, 1965.

TAYLOR, N., *Narcotics*, Delta, New York, 1963.

WILNER, D. M., and G. G. KASSEBAUM, *Narcotics*, McGraw-Hill Book Company, New York, 1965.

YABLONSKY, L. *The Tunnel Back: Synanon*, The Macmillan Company, New York, 1965.

THE SEDATIVES

Barbiturates as Addicting Drugs, Public Health Service Publication 545, 1963.

"Dependence on Barbiturates and Other Sedatives," AMA Committee on Alcoholism and Addiction, *J. Am. Med. Assoc.*, 193:673–677 (Aug. 23), 1965.

FORT, J., "The Problem of Barbiturates in the U.S.A.," *Bull. Narcotics*, U.N. Dept. Social Affairs, 16:17 (January–March), 1964

THE STIMULANTS AND COCAINE

"Addiction to Amphetamines," *Brit. Med. J.*, 5354:339 (Aug. 17), 1963.

CONNELL, P. H., "Clinical Manifestations and Treatment of Amphetamine Type of Dependence," *J. Am. Med. Assoc.*, 196:718 (May 23), 1966.

"Dependence on Amphetamines and Other Stimulant Drugs," AMA Committee on Alcoholism and Addiction, *J. Am. Med. Assoc.*, 197:1023–1027 (Sept. 19), 1966.

KRAMER, J. C., V. S. FISCHMAN, and D. C. LITTLEFIELD, "Amphetamine Abuse: Pattern and Effects of High Doses Taken Intravenously," *J. Am. Med. Assoc.*, 201:305–309 (July 31), 1967.

LEAKE, C., *The Amphetamines*, Charles C Thomas, Publisher, Springfield, Ill., 1958.

THE SNIFFERS

ACKERLEY, W. C., and G. GIBSON, "Lighter Fluid Sniffing," *Am. J. Psychiat.*, 120:1056 (May), 1964.

"Glue Sniffing," *Natl. Clearinghouse for Poison Control Centers Bull.*, February–March, 1962.

JACOBYNER, H., *et al.*, "Glue Sniffing," *N.Y. State J. Med.*, 63:2415 (August), 1963.

MESSENGALE, O. N., *et al.*, "Physical and Psychologic Factors in Glue Sniffing," *New Engl. J. Med.*, 269:1340 (Dec. 19), 1963.